DISCARD

D1171157

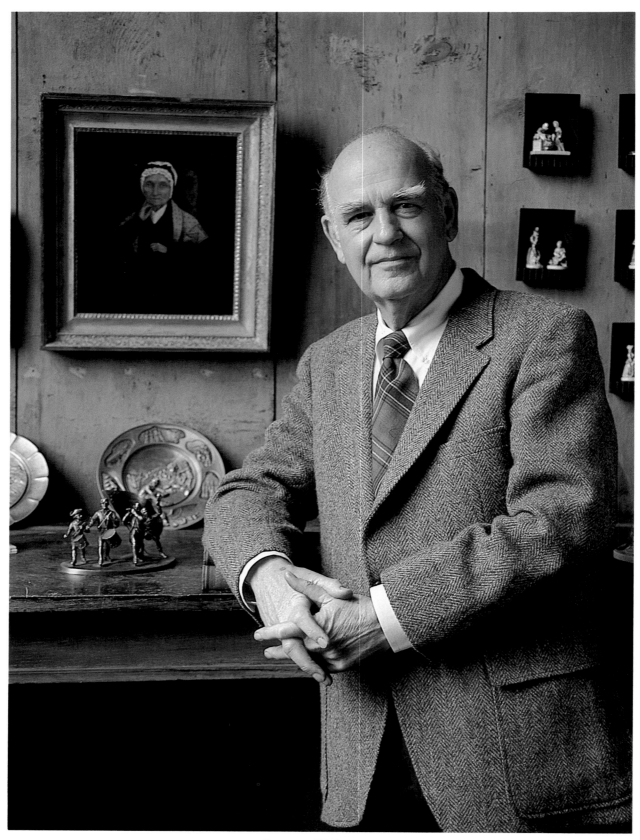

Prescott W. Baston
Marblehead

THE SEBASTIAN MINIATURE COLLECTION

A Guide to Identifying, Understanding and Enjoying
Sebastian Miniatures

by Dr. Glenn S. Johnson

**This volume is number _9416_ of a
strictly limited edition of 10,000 books.**

Photographer: Russell Brett
Designer: Joseph Havens
Production Director: Frank Casey
Library of Congress Catalog Card Number: 82-81555
International Standard Book No.: ISBN 0-914275-08-2
First Edition, Limited to 10,000 Copies
Printed and bound in the United States of America

This book is dedicated to Beth, who understood

Contents

The History of Sebastian Miniatures

Historian J. P. O'Donnell writes, "The gap between the generations, unless it is to become a chasm and make history meaningless, must be bridged. Each generation owes an after-action report to the generation that follows."

In the case of Prescott Baston and his Sebastian Miniatures, the term "after-action" is partially misleading. After over 40 years of creative and productive toil, the "action" has never been as active. Baston spends today's hours designing new figurines and training craftsmen in a modern art studio in Lee, New Hampshire. He flies Boeing 747 jumbo jets that cross the continent in a matter of hours. His televised image is relayed to private homes around the country.

His miniature figurines are advertised in slick "collectible" magazines and are the subjects of "collectibles dealers'" newsletters. Shining bright lucite cabinets display his work in specialized gift shops and galleries. Tens of thousands of names, addresses and zip codes of his collecting public are stored in an electronic computer that prints labels every three months directing a "Society Newsletter" to those names. A large, modern business has been built around his Sebastian Miniatures.

But the generation gap *does* exist. Baston was born in 1909, the year William Howard Taft took office as President of the United States. The federal income tax (the 16th amendment to the Constitution) was ratified four years later. In 1917, when Baston was eight, the United States entered World War I.

He was a 20-year-old art student in Boston at the time of the Wall Street Crash, an event plunging our country into a ten-year Great Depression. These are *not* the times of most of us. The majority of our current population was born after the Depression. Most of us do not remember those harsh years and thus cannot even hope to feel what that America was like.

Yet strangely, and perhaps this helps to explain at least part of America's current fascination with Sebastian Miniatures, Prescott Baston does bridge the gap. With a boyhood and youth fully formed in the old America, his work lives freshly in the new.

How old was the America of the Thirties, the decade in which he produced his first Sebastians?

President Herbert Hoover in 1930 was the first president of the United States to have a telephone on his desk. The United States boasted the seventeenth largest army in the world behind, among others, Spain, Czechoslovakia and Rumania. Washington, D.C.'s airport handled 250 passengers a day and every stewardess was a registered nurse.

There were no power mowers, home air-conditioning units, automatic dishwashers, clothes driers, electric blankets, clock radios, nylons, drip-dry clothes, frozen foods, automatic coffee makers, vinyl floors, ballpoint pens, Xerox machines, hi-fi stereo sets, Scotch tape, color camera film, tape recorders or home hair driers.

Radio was just beginning and phonographs had to be wound by hand. A housewife had only a carpet sweeper as a mechanical help and men stood up to give women seats on a streetcar. When men drove their new Chevrolets ($445 F.O.B. Detroit) to work they could usually find a convenient parking spot. A nickle bought a loaf of bread, a cup of coffee or a copy of *Saturday Evening Post, Collier's* or *Liberty.* An income of $5,000 bought comforts unknown today.

And, up to 1938, amazingly little had changed. The stock market had crashed in 1929, and the American economy and American people had all they could do to stay where they were, never mind growth and progress. These were the years Baston lived, learned and worked in preparation for his life's work.

9 Court Street, Arlington, Massachusetts

Prescott Baston, 19 (1928)

Getting Ready
1909–1937

Prescott Woodbury Baston was born in 1909 at 9 Court Street, Arlington, Massachusetts, a town that is part of Greater Boston.

His father was a miniaturist for Olmsted Brothers, the architectural firm that designed New York's Central Park and Cloisters and Boston's Public Gardens. He designed and created microminiature models of buildings, bridges, terraces and anything else that was part of an architect's plan.

Baston does not remember any formal art training as a child, but does recall watching his father work. At age 12 in the sixth grade at Russell School in Arlington, he vividly remembers drawing the bottom half of a phonograph as an assignment and being mightily pleased with the results. His interst in art seemed to be "always there."

During his Arlington High School years (1924–1927), Baston continued his two great interests, art and literature. It was here that he read all of Charles Dickens' writings for the first time (he was to re-read all of Dickens several times in later years) and studied many of the Shakespearean plays. He claims he is a "born ham" and got involved with amateur theatrics at the time. His art consisted of sketching everyday objects and scenes, all on a very informal self-taught basis.

He graduated from Arlington in 1927 and continued working at his high school job at the Loft Drug Store soda fountain. Based on recommendations from his teachers, he was offered a scholarship at the Normal Art School in Boston. Baston did not want to teach for a living, and he refused the offer. In 1928 he entered the Vesper George School of Art, a Boston practical art school. He attended classes part-time and continued working at the drug store.

He left Loft's and joined his father on a part-time basis at Olmsted's in Brookline with the rest of his time spent at Vesper George. The stock market crash in October ended any thoughts Baston may have had of continuing his formal education. In rapid succession, his father died in 1930, he joined Olmsted full-time and he left Vesper George. For the next eight years he was to work at five different jobs, all aimed at providing an income for his mother and himself.

In 1930, at age 21, Baston worked on miniature models of the campuses of Exeter and Deerfield Academies. During this period, he learned and practiced many of the techniques of miniaturization; scale, perspective, color, materials. The time was the Depression, however, and work at any architectural firm was unreliable at best, especially for a novice. He was forced on to different work where he could find it.

From 1931 through 1932, Baston worked as an all-around handyman for Francis Hicks, a Boston interior decorator. It would glorify the job to say that Baston furthered his artistic and compositional skills. What he really did was move things around, deliver products and parcels and any other project Francis Hicks could find for a strapping young man.

From 1933 to 1936 Baston worked at the Electric Time Company in Boston. He delivered clocks to Boston stores and installed custom-built clocks. In 1935 he was given the assignment of designing and sculpting an ornate frame for a large clock to be installed at the Medford Cooperative Bank. He remembers being paid seventy-five dollars for the job, an enormous sum at the time even though he worked months on it. The clock is still there.

The work at Electric Time was sporadic and Baston took on two more jobs in 1935. First, he and several friends started to move furniture professionally in the Boston and the Cape Cod area. Always physically strong, he recalls moving three pianos one hot day and wrestling around 300-pound casks of turpentine. He moved furniture until 1938, covering a four-year period of highly physical labor.

MURAL for the Boston Trade School for Girls just completed by Prescott Baston of the WPA federal art project. It shows a scene in the Public Garden in the 70's.

The June 19, 1938 Boston Herald *rotogravure section included a photo of Baston's Girls Trade School mural of the Boston Garden in the 1870's.*

He also applied for and received several commissions from Franklin Delano Roosevelt's Federal Art Project to paint large murals in the Boston area. In addition to several panels of animals and birds for Boston public schools, he painted four 8- by 6-foot panels for the Collector of the Port of Boston in the Customs House Tower. He painted two panels for the Haverhill High School (now City Hall) that are still there and one wall of the Brighton High School Library. In June 1938, he completed an 8-by-28-foot mural of the Boston Public Garden for the Boston Trade School for Girls.

This brought Baston up to 1938, the year of his first Sebastian Miniature and his full-time employment for the rest of his life (except for a four-year war job stint). What can be said for this background? What made Baston "ready" for his life's work?

He was born and raised in Boston New England, providing not only a geographical but a cultural bent that would sustain him through a lifetime.

He had a strongly artistic leaning. There can be no doubt that his father's profession influenced him, just as there can be no doubt that he possessed an aptitude for the arts. When the Normal Art School offered him a scholarship, it had become obvious that others had recognized his skills.

This aptitude was developed at a formal art school where he widened his knowledge of materials, color and techniques. His work on architectural models sharpened his fascination with the problems of miniaturization. The granting of federal art fund projects meant that he had to compete against other artists eager for work. And once that project was granted, he had to plan and compose artistic scenes that told a story and portrayed that story for all to see.

His love of history, literature and theatrics would appear later in his presidents and Williamsburg characters; his Dickens, Mark Twain and House of Seven Gables "families;"and his Shakespearean couples.

And finally, he was ready for artistic commercial labor. From heavy manual labor to delivering clocks to completing federal murals on time, he had learned that an artist is a person who makes his living at art. A hard worker bent on making money during the Depression, he easily transferred that energy to his Sebastian Miniatures. A new America was coming of age and Prescott Baston was ready to come of age with it.

Store Sales, The War and Marblehead
1938–1950

The year 1938 marked the last year of the Depression and the beginning of the World War II era. German dictator Adolf Hitler annexed Austria and British Prime Minister Neville Chamberlain journeyed to Munich mistakenly seeking "peace in our time." Orson Welles scared the country with his radio broadcast of a Martian invasion, while Edgar Bergen and Charlie McCarthy, George Burns and Gracie Allen, Jack Benny and Fred Allen kept them laughing. Walt Disney introduced the first full-length animated cartoon movie "Snow White and the Seven Dwarfs" and Spencer Tracy appeared with the youthful Mickey Rooney in "Boys Town." A newcomer named Bob Hope gained national prominence in "The Big Broadcast of 1938."

A woman who owned the Shaker Glen House restaurant in Woburn, Massachusetts, knew that a young man in her church had an artistic background of sorts. One day, following services, she asked if he would agree to designing a small set of figurines depicting a Shaker Couple.

Baston remembers going to his basement in Arlington and designing a simple pair using photos from a book he owned describing the Shaker religious movement. His first impulse was to portray them accurately but also to design them so they were easy to cast and paint.

The woman saw them a few weeks later and ordered four dozen to sell and give away to restaurant guests. He built some rubber molds, cast the figurines and painted them, all during the evening after he was done with his day job. When the woman paid him ("they were very inexpensive"), he was pleased to have made money with his art. When she came back a few weeks later and ordered a thousand, he was flabbergasted. He spent more and more time in his studio, casting and painting the figurines.

One day, on the advice of the Shaker Glen House restaurant owner, Baston visited Carbone, a wholesale gift distributor in Boston. He asked if they would be interested in a line of miniature figurines portraying famous American couples. When he showed Hans Laaby, Carbone president, the George and Martha Washington, John Alden and Priscilla and Williamsburg pairs he had just designed, Laaby told him: "Go back and design a dozen different pairs. We need a line."

Baston designed another five pairs and Carbone accepted his work. They planned for an introduction at the Boston Gift Show in March, 1939. Now we should look briefly at the "gift industry" as it existed in those earliest days.

No gift shops as such had yet emerged; gift counters, if there were any, were small departments of larger department stores. The Depression years demanded that most gifts be inexpensive objects, designed as simple expressions of caring.

The "mail order industry" as we know it today existed then of a few stores such as Sears & Roebuck that specialized in selling clothes and tools to farmers.

Collectibles were those items that people chose to acquire, sort, classify and display simply because they wanted to. Only the stamp and coin marketeers offered convenient catalogs, buying services and aftermarket dealers where a collector could conveniently buy an old issue. President Franklin Delano Roosevelt helped popularize the infant stamp collecting hobby.

Practically everything was paid for by cash or check. Credit as such was non-existent except for food and some articles of clothing. If you asked a gift counter clerk of that time if she accepted Visa, Mastercard or American Express, she would not believe the intricate system you explained to her.

Carbone imported its gifts from Europe (usually Italy), stored them in a Boston warehouse and hired salesmen to sell them around the country. The company owned permanent showrooms in New York, Chicago and Los Angeles. Its salesmen would ride trains to Kansas City, New Orleans and St. Louis and set-up temporary displays in hotel rooms. Buyers would come to these rooms by invitation, study the displayed wares and purchase for the coming season. A traveling salesman with his bulging sample cases was a familiar sight at any train station.

Prescott Baston, age 30, in his 1939 Arlington home basement, examining a casting of an early "Ben Franklin" figurine. Ornate wall decoration experiments hang on the back wall and a large prototype of what would later be scaled-down to Huck Finn's "Jim" is under the table.

The March, 1939, Boston Gift Show resulted in three events. First, Baston received orders for several thousands of his miniature figurines. Second, Carbone decided to sell the line nationally. Third, Baston decided to quit all his jobs, set-up a professional studio in his Arlington basement and begin a career designing and producing "Baston Figurines."

But it was decided that "Baston Figurines" was not an adequate title for the line. Baston's name was too awkward for a much-used tradename. In 1939, Baston titled his line "Sebastian Miniatures," a name that now lives independently of its creator.

During 1939, '40 and '41, Baston designed more pairs, traveled some with Carbone salesmen, and established a production system in his Arlington basement.

He employed up to six people in the morning and the same number in the afternoon to make rubber molds from master designs, cast figurines from the molds and clean them with a knife in preparation for painting. He discovered that the large figurine areas could be painted in a painter's home, eliminating his need for a larger studio. He also learned that miniature detailing of his figurines (eyes, lips, eyebrows) was popular among his buyers and that the task could not be trusted to an experienced home painter.

In 1939, Adolf Hitler invaded Poland, beginning World War II in Europe. That year, Baston met and began courting Marjorie Keyes while Sebastian Miniatures continued to grow, both in numbers of subjects and in sales volume. Baston recalls that a buyer could purchase a dozen sets of pairs for twelve dollars.

Baston designed a set of six birds in 1941 and "Secrets," a pair of kittens. Carbone had told him he needed figurines in the Sebastian line to compete with other animal figurine imports and Baston complied, but the experiment amounted to nothing. Baston designed a larger grouping of Christmas Nativity subjects, but that too was discontinued in favor of his miniature people.

Frank Sinatra sang "I'll Never Smile Again," Winston Churchill was elected British Prime Minister, Dunkirk was evacuated, the Battle of Britain raged over London and Norway, Denmark, Holland, Belgium and France fell to the Germans. On December 7, 1941, the Japanese bombed Pearl Harbor. On December 8, the United States declared war on Japan and on December 11 on Germany and Italy. The United States was to be totally involved in the massive war effort the next four years.

Baston and Marjorie went ahead with their plans and were married on December 21. Events continued to move quickly. The couple moved from Baston's Arlington home to a small apartment in Cambridge and he volunteered for a job in the Massachusetts Institute of Technology's war effort. He was to immerse himself for the next two-and-a-half years, working up to 56 hours a week, on a variety of MIT projects involving miniature design and craftsmanship. One such project was a system for a highly accurate bomb release, later used on Allied air raids over Germany.

Baston was not anxious to continue producing his miniatures over these years, but Carbone was insistent. All European gift imports were stopped at the beginning of the war, and Sebastian Miniatures was one of the few lines available to meet a figurine gift demand. Marjorie stepped in and when Baston went to MIT in the morning, she left their Cambridge apartment to supervise the workers in the Arlington studio. She maintained all production and sales records and kept the books. Armando Carli was in charge of mold-making and up to six people worked in the studio at peak periods. At night the couple would discuss the day's work. This was to go on through the middle of 1944.

In 1942, Baston designed a "Children's Band" for Carbone that resembled a German import. In 1943, the couple moved to another apartment in Winchester, and, the same year, Baston designed a Christmas ornament for the line portraying one of Raphael's Madonna paintings. In August, 1944, Baston accepted a job as Personnel Manager for the J. W. Greer Company in Cambridge, a sheet-metal fabricating company that produced miniature components under a sub-contract to Raytheon. On June 6, the Allies invaded Europe and in December, the Germans mounted their last great offense in the Ardennes forest, the Battle of the Bulge. U.S. cars bore A, B or C gas rationing stickers, people lined up for blocks to buy rationed cigarettes, FDR defeated Tom Dewey for his fourth term as president and the two war songs that dominated the Hit Parade that year were "I'll Walk Alone" and "I'll Be Seeing You."

The next year, 1945, was one of the 20th Century's most significant. In rapid order, President Roosevelt, Mussolini and Hitler died, Germany surrendered, President Truman ordered the atomic bomb dropped on Hiroshima and Nagasaki and then Japan surrendered. The war was over.

Prescott W. Baston, Jr. (quickly "Woody" to everyone) was born on January 24 of that year and, in September, Baston resigned his war job at Greer. With Woody on the scene, the Winchester apartment had become too crowded, and Baston began looking for a permanent home and studio location. He searched Boston's North Shore and discovered a beautiful home on the square surrounding historic Abbot Hall in Marblehead and a vacant two-story building on a small street off the other side of the square.

The town of Marblehead is a small (22,000), picturesque village on the Atlantic coast, famous especially for its 18th century buildings and its 20th century yachting.

Baston purchased and renovated these two buildings and in 1946 the three Bastons moved to Marblehead. He equipped the two-story building and basement with benches, shelving, desks and filing cabinets and began full post-war production of Sebastian Miniatures in earnest. While continuing his ongoing relationship with Carbone, he also signed a contract to produce "Folks in Little"® by Sebastian for Schmid Brothers, another Boston gift distributor. He designed and produced his Dickens collection for distribution by Carbone and his Farmer and Wife for Schmid. More and more retail stores (mostly in the Boston area) began stocking and selling Sebastians. As a forerunner of things to come, he was approached by the Puritan Candy Company in Somerville. At their request, he designed and produced 300 figurines of the company's trademark, a Puritan woman at her spinning wheel. The Spinner was given away to candy store customers to remind them of their suppliers. As such, it was the forerunner of his later commercial work for Jell-O, Johnson & Johnson, *Saturday Evening Post* and *Reader's Digest.*

The years 1946 to 1950 marked the most productive years in the history of Sebastian Miniatures gift shop design and sales prior to the recent explosion of collector interest in the 1980's. During these five years, Baston designed an astounding one hundred designs for Carbone and Schmid customers. Included during this period, in addition to the Dickens collection, were the Shakespearean couples, Mark Twain's Family, the Rittenhouses, House of Seven Gables, Washington Irving group and Famous Americans.

A typical Marblehead street of beautiful 18th century homes and a view of its harbor, famous in America's China Trade history and later as a world yachting center.

When he completed his first group of Dickens figurines and the Copperfield cottage, he designed a mechanical "locking" system of hexagonal (six-sided) bases that fit into each other and the cottage backdrop. He immediately applied for a patent on this design and inscribed "PAT. PEND." into each figurine base. In 1953 he was finally informed that the patent was not going to be granted and he removed the words from the base. Any Dickens pieces now bearing those two words are vintage 1946–1953.

Beginning in 1947, he designed his Washington, Lincoln, Roosevelt, Jefferson and Jackson as part of his "Famous American" series, a series that would continue into the '60's. In 1948 he designed a "Republican Victory" figurine of an elephant squashing a donkey. To hedge against a highly unlikely outcome, he also designed a donkey on top. After Harry Truman had pulled off one of history's great political upsets, Baston wished the country would have known beforehand. He had sold very few "Democratic Victorys."

Baston designed sets of regional characters (Pennsylvania Amish, midwest farmers and fishers) for Schmid and "Pilgrims," his first of many couples on a single base for gift shop sales. For his Shakespearean Couples he chose the popular Romeo, Juliet and Falstaff along with the lesser-known Touchstone, Malvolio and Countess Olivia. His six Mark Twain characters were from *Tom Sawyer* and *Huckleberry Finn*, and his Washington Irving series were taken from Irving's two short stories, *Rip Van Winkle* and *The Legend of Sleepy Hollow*. His Paul Bunyan and Clown, so popular in the late 1970's, were created as regional characters, and his three Nursery Rhyme scenes were originally designed to be placed atop music boxes. All of his retail designs were subjects Baston was fond of and also believed to be of national interest.

But as all of this was occurring, Baston was also receiving an increasing amount of commercial commissions to design a special figurine and then produce it in large volume for one customer.

Following his Puritan Spinner, Baston accepted commercial jobs from R. H. Stearns, the Necco Candy Company, Boston's Shawmut Bank, Jordan Marsh, the John Hancock Insurance Company and the Irwin Neisler Drug Company.

R. H. Stearns was a prosperous high-fashion department store when Baston accepted his first commercial commissions from them in 1947. His "Godey Couple" portrayed a young Bostonian couple while out shopping and the figurine bears an "1847" in the base to mark the centennial of the store's founding. Baston's "Dahl Series" portrayed in three dimensions the caricatures John Dahl, the *Boston Herald* cartoonist, had created for Stearns. The popular Swan Boat was first designed for Stearns.

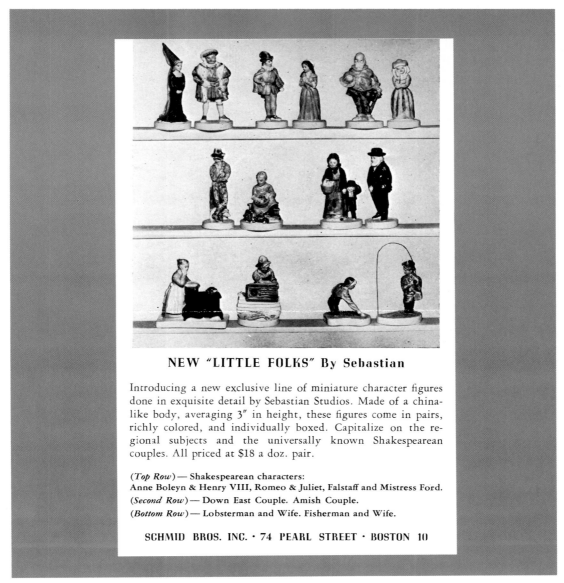

A March, 1947 ad by Schmid Brothers describes the "New 'Little Folks' by Sebastian." The ad tells dealers to "Capitalize on the regional subjects and the universally known Shakespearean couples. All priced at $18 a dozen pair."

Necco Candy in Cambridge ordered an early candy store scene for use in its many sales promotions. Jordan Marsh, the Boston department store, had created its "Observer" from the thousands of "sidewalk superintendents" who watched workmen build the new store. It was the first of many Sebastian-Jordan Marsh Observers.

During these years, Baston designed the three figurines that, until 1980, were to result in his largest volumes of production. Altogether he produced 12,000 John Hancocks, 45,000 Mr. Obocells and 90,000 Shawmut Indians. Nothing in the retail gift line came close to approaching these numbers.

As the Forties came to an end and America embarked into the Fifties, Sebastian Miniatures history can be described thusly:

- An encouraging start (especially following the Depression) of a line of retail gifts.
- A holding action during World War II.
- A fresh start in 1946 with two fine gift distributors and a new studio in Marblehead.
- An explosion of designs with broad historic and literary appeal for sale in stores nationally.
- A growing awareness of and dependence on fewer design—higher volume—more profitable commercial jobs.

Eventually the commercial business won out. An examination of Baston's old ledgers indicates the last entry for sales to Carbone as April 17, 1950, a retail gift relationship that had existed for over thirteen years. The last entry for Schmid was December 20, 1950, ending a four-year relationship.

Meanwhile, things were in swift transition elsewhere. On June 8, 1948, Milton Berle stepped in front of a television camera for the first time on the "Texaco Star Theater." Before he ended his Tuesday night show in 1956, the United States' communications and electronic industries would change our comprehension of "the past" forever.

Joe Louis retired as champ, ending his twelve-year reign. The North Koreans crossed the thirty-eighth parallel in June, 1950, and President Harry Truman recalled later that the most difficult decision he ever made, including the one to drop the world's first atomic bomb, was to send troops into Korea. By Christmas, draft boards in average big cities were calling up to 200 men a day.

Two new terms came into usage: "H-bomb" and "taking the Fifth." President Truman authorized the Atomic Engergy Commission to produce the new hydrogen bomb, and the Supreme Court ruled that under the Fifth Amendment no one could be forced to testify against himself.

The decade known as the Flaming Forties, which actually had flared into global flames, gave way to the one that was going to be the Fabulous Fifties.

Commercial Sales
1951-1968

Although Baston remained active in his retail sales efforts, 1951 marked a clear shift in emphasis to commercial sales. From 1938 to 1950, when Carbone and Schmid gift distribution dominated design activity, 148 of his first 165 designs were general in subject. Only seventeen designs during that twelve-year period were commercial designs. But in 1951 alone he created fourteen commercial designs. From 1951 to 1968, the year that almost all Sebastian design activity ground to a halt, he created a remarkable 137 figurines primarily aimed at commercial sales. Put another way, only ten percent of all his designs were commercial from 1938 to 1950, while almost seventy percent were commercial after that.

More importantly, the shift in Sebastian production was even more marked. As his commercial business grew and the production runs became focussed on groups of workers producing one design, he more and more used his small-order retail business to "fill-in" between commercial jobs.

This shift in emphasis would not be important except for its profound effect on old Sebastian Miniatures now available to current collectors. The question must be asked, how many old Sebastian Miniatures still exist? The nature of commercial versus retail has many ripple effects on this question.

In the first place, all commercial designs were meant to be given away and also meant to promote a product or a service. Gifts are designed to create an emotion in a shopper's mind or heart and endear the giver to the receiver. The commercial design was not meant to be kept or displayed over the years. The retail design was. In today's collector activities, the commercial designs are very hard to find; they usually are the real rarities. The retail designs generally are more profuse.

In the second place, where the commercial designs are blatantly commercial they are even less likely to be found. 90,000 Shawmut Indians (SML 93) were produced from 1947 until the present. The miniature is an attractive bust of an American Indian. The reason a person received it, however, was because he deposited money in a Shawmut Bank account. The last thing he had in mind in the transaction was obtaining a Sebastian Miniature. Old Shawmut Indian pieces do exist, however, because of their innate attractiveness. They were kept by many people.

The S.O.S. Lady (SML 303), on the other hand, was designed for blatantly commercial use. When the scouring pad company planned an advertising campaign in *Reader's Digest* magazine, they received a complimentary offer by the magazine to help promote the cleanser. In 1959, the *Digest* ordered 3,000 figurines from Baston. Just before the first ad ran, the magazine sent a letter to 3,000 of S.O.S.'s largest customers saying: "When you see this woman in *Reader's Digest*, remember that S.O.S. is helping you attract customers to your store and helping you sell profitable scouring pads."

The people who received these miniatures were typically men in high-pressure merchandising jobs. It's safe to conclude that Mrs. S.O.S. was not displayed or stored with great care or tender concern. She was either thrown away immediately or knocked around in some child's playbox until broken beyond repair. Not many exist today, over twenty years later.

With all this as a background for the direction Sebastians were to take until 1978, we will continue tracing this history.

With the end of distribution by Carbone and Schmid, Baston appointed H. P. & H. F. Hunt, a local independent sales group, to service his Boston-area gift shops. With this group acquiring sporadic orders for Sebastian retail items, he turned his attention to commercial sales. He reasoned accurately that the greatest potential for commercial advertising business was located in New York's Madison Avenue advertising agencies. Young & Rubicam ordered 2,000 pieces of a "Chiquita Banana" design for their United Fruit Company account. The success of this job, both at Baston's end and the warm reception by merchandising officials, led to over ten years of continued trips to Madison Avenue and nights in the old Gramatan Hotel in Bronxville. Almost all of his many commercial commissions outside Boston (*Reader's Digest*, Jello-O, Johnson & Johnson, Curtis Publishing) were to progress from this start.

Prescott Baston at Boston store promoting radio station WEEI figurines. Heloise ("Mother") Parker, station cooking expert, examines her likeness.

One of the Sebastian painters decorates a "Jesse Buffum" WEEI figurine at a Boston store personal appearance. Baston personally autographed all Sebastians bought at these promotional events.

Two Jell-O ads from 1952 issues of the Saturday Evening Post. The "Having a Little Trouble, Mac?" ad resulted in Baston's Lost in the Kitchen (SML 200) and "Hey, take it easy, Junior!" in his Jell-O Baby (SML 202).

Boston radio station WEEI, like all other radio stations suffering slumping advertising reverses as the result of television's exploding popularity, planned a city-wide promotion. Baston was ordered to design caricatures of seven of the station's most popular personalities. The WEEI series today is one of the very popular rare collectible groupings.

In 1951, Baston had designed two series of three Raphael Madonnas and three 19th century mothers for his retail stores. In 1952 he sculpted three miniature replicas of the historical Rogers Groups with which he strongly identified. John Rogers, a 19th century American artist, sculpted compact groupings of ordinary people doing ordinary things. At Rogers's insistence, his bulky eighteen-inch-high groups were cast in a brownish plaster rather than the bronze or fired ceramic demanded by the critics. He wanted his work to be in the homes of thousands of Americans rather than the exclusive property of an elite few. Baston's studies of the Rogers Groups in school and on display in the Essex Institute in nearby Salem had engendered an early design style and also the desire to have his work available to many. Later, Rogers was elected to the National Sculpture Society in New York as "one who had touched the hearts of millions with his sculpture."

Following the success of the Chiquita Banana promotion, Young & Rubicam planned an advertising campaign for General Foods' Jell-O brand that required thirteen Sebastians over the next five years. When Jell-O ran an ad showing a Scottish girl studying her budget, the headline said, "Now's the Time for Jell-O." Before the ad appeared nationally, Jell-O sent Sebastians to its top 3,000 national accounts reminding them "...when you see this lass in your magazines and newspapers, remember how Jell-O is helping you sell. Stock up Now!"

The Jell-O series, Baston's longest series except for his Charles Dickens Family, is valued today because of its rarity (commercial) and also because of the attractiveness of all thirteen designs.

To give us an idea of where these times stood in our past, Vice-presidential nominee Richard M. Nixon appeared on television in 1952 to deliver his "Checkers" speech, and Dwight D. Eisenhower, hero of World War II seven years before, ended a twenty-year Democratic rule in Washington. Arthur Godfrey maintained two top TV shows and comedienne Lucille Ball's "I Love Lucy" topped the rating charts for the first time, a position she was to hold for five years.

In 1953, Baston canceled his Hunt Brothers gift shop sales contract and employed two sales organizations, one local and one national.

Thomas Wiles of Cohasset maintained gift shop sales in the Boston area. His job was to keep Sebastian stocks at a good level in stores and to open new dealerships where he could. Baston's relationship with the Copley Advertising Company in Boston was much more ambitious. Working with L. E. Sissman, Baston began an independent direct mail program of sales to stores and commercial institutions.

Baston and Sissman prepared a four-page catalog that was mailed to thousands of gift shops around the country. It advertised the opportunity "to share increased profits, greater volume, repeat business and year-round sales through Sebastian Studio's exclusive Story-Series Plan." This brochure foresaw America's collecting boom of the 1970's. Speaking twenty years ahead of his time, Baston wrote: "Our line has a special appeal to collectors because each figure is part of a connected series."

Baston and Sissman also conducted an advertising campaign promoting the commercial business. Although the "Premium and Incentive" market was not organized then as it is today, certain specialists were already putting sales contests and product promotions together.

That year Baston also designed what was to become his most popular series, the Godey Children. The Hummel children, first introduced in the United States by Marshal Field, Chicago, in 1935, three years before the Shaker pair, had been growing in popularity following the return of G.I.'s from Germany during the war and after. Baston had been encouraged by his dealers to design American kids in a larger scale than his miniatures. The Godey kids were inspired by the illustrations of 19th century fashions in *The Godey's Ladies Book*, the fashion magazine of its era.

Plummers, the fine china and glass store in Manhattan, asked Baston to design a serious sculpture of a nativity. The resulting scene is regarded by many as his miniaturization masterpiece. In 1961 he broke it down into less expensive components, the Manger, Wisemen and Shepherds. He also designed "The Doctor" from Sir Luke Fildes' famous painting in London's Tate Gallery for the Irwin Neisler Drug Company. When converted to retail sales, the design became one of the best sellers.

Judging from sales records and design activity, this period must be judged the most active in the history of Sebastian Miniatures in Marblehead. Baston had introduced and built up his retail line with over 150 designs and hundreds of dealers. After starts with Carbone, Schmid and the Hunts, he was running sales on his own with a local salesman and a national selling program.

His studio was producing efficiently with ten to twelve employees in the shop and many more home painters fully employed. His Jell-O, Shawmut Bank and Neisler commercial jobs were providing large volume

HERE IS
your OPPORTUNITY

to share...

- **Increased Profits**
- **Greater Volume** • **Repeat Business**
- **Year-Round Sales**

through

SEBASTIAN STUDIO'S
Exclusive

STORY-SERIES PLAN

Here is *your* opportunity to participate in a new sales plan that is unique . . . in Sebastian Studio's Story-Series Plan . . . the only merchandising plan that helps you reach a responsive new clientele of *repeat* buyers right in your own community — people with ready money to spend in your shop. No financial risk whatever is involved. If you are not entirely satisfied with the line, you may return all unsold items within fourteen days after receipt for full credit. You will be backed with a national publicity and promotion campaign . . . with promotional literature and attractive point-of-purchase display material . . . with the growing prestige of Sebastian Miniatures throughout America.

Read how the Sebastian STORY-SERIES
Plan works for you . . . . .

Page one of the 1953 Story-Series Plan mailer. Baston was twenty years ahead of his time by planning collectible series. The back of the brochure lists retail prices of Little Mother: $4.00; Sistine Madonna: $3.00; In the Candy Store: $2.00; Sampling the Stew: $1.75; David and Dora Copperfield: $1.50; and Old Salt: $1.25!

An April 24, 1953 ad in Printer's Ink *magazine tells How to Exploit Your Trademark. "Sebastian Miniatures build lasting goodwill with your customers, dealers, wholesalers, employees—for years to come!" The corporations pictured include Necco Candy, John Hancock Insurance, Jordan Marsh, the Shawmut Bank, Irwin Neisler Drugs, United Fruit, WEEI, Pontiac, Tabasco Sauce and Jell-O. (It is interesting to note the Marblehead telephone number: 0004-W. The call was handled by a switchboard operator!)*

and his ongoing Madison Avenue business demanded continual trips to Manhattan.

Along with design, production and sales, Baston made many personal appearances around the country. From 1950 to 1955, he was part of two public speaker program agencies that placed public speakers nationally. A 1950 flier describes "a clear-cut, fascinating explanation of what modern thinking in architecture, in color, in decorative accessories should mean to you."

Also during this time, the country had been menaced into a Red Scare, led by Senator Joseph McCarthy of Wisconsin. The televised Army hearings (McCarthy, Roy Cohn, and Joseph Welch) of 1955 plunged the United States into its lowest point of guilt-by-association and held television viewers spellbound. Davy Crockett, Sid Caesar, Imogene Coca and Jackie Gleason also held us spellbound. A relatively unknown bandleader named Lawrence Welk first appeared in front of the camera, and Bill Haley's "Rock Around the Clock" on a sound track behind the "Blackboard Jungle" camera signalled a new era in music. Elvis Presley followed in 1956.

From that year through 1959, Baston began a busy commercial schedule beginning with Johnson & Johnson. In rapid succession he produced Robin Hood and Little John, Robin Hood and Friar Tuck, the Texcel Tape Boy, the Permacel Tower of Tape, the Rarical Balcksmith, Praying Hands and Arthritic Hands for the New Jersey company. In 1958 he converted a series of his 1939 and 1940 early pairs designs and mounted them together on an ornate base design. All of this was proposed to the Essex County National Bank in Peabody. As planned, Baston would have produced a pen and pencil set for the bank's customers with a recessed oval that held the interchangeable pairs. When the bank decided not to go ahead with the promotion, Baston sold the converted pairs through his retail dealers.

In 1959, Baston continued his commercial business with a series of five figures for the gift shop in the Museum of the City of New York. To this day, critics consider the Peter Stuyvesant and Verazzano of that series among his best detailed work. His Madison Avenue commercial ventures also resulted that year in a series of *Reader's Digest* commissions. His designs for Siesta Coffee, S.O.S. Scouring Pads, Fleischman's Margarine and Alcoa Wrap resulted in the production of almost 10,000 figurines that year alone.

Armando Carli, of the Arlington and MIT days, works on a mold of the Shawmut Indian. Other molds on the bench include St. Teresa, Covered Bridge, Stimalose, St. Sebastian, Santa Claus, Baby Buggy of 1850 and The Pilgrims.

Three Sebastian painters work on 1954's Jell-O Whale. Beth Haley, the center painter, reemerged in 1981 as a professional restorer of damaged Sebastians.

Presenting

P R E S C O T T W.

BASTON

"Design Around Us"

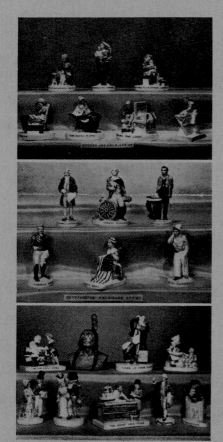

NEW BEAUTY IN YOUR LIFE. Here is the colorful, dramatic story of modern design for *living* — how it started, how it grew, how it affects all of us today. Here is a clear-cut, fascinating explanation of what modern thinking in architecture, in color, in decorative accessories should mean to you. Here is the startling story of what it can do for you — for your home, your family, your way of living.

FROM THE GROUND UP. Mr. Baston begins at the beginning. His sparkling talk puts first things first, explains the *careful thinking* that lies behind all good design. Then he goes on to tell how you can make this thinking work for *you*. His masterly understanding of art and architecture, both modern and classic, makes his lecture more than just a talk. In fact, it is actually *a one-lesson course* in the elements of modern design — but far more entertaining than any course you've known.

MR. BASTON'S exhaustive knowledge of his field is the result of many years' study in our finest schools...of years spent as a landscape architect...of a successful career in mural-painting...of twelve exciting years devoted to sculpture in miniature of some 200 exquisite figurines. His brilliant, instructive lectures abound with artistic insight, unusual information, human interest, and the true tang of Yankee wit and humor.

EXCLUSIVE MANAGEMENT

flora frame

Club Program Bureau

154 NEWBURY STREET, BOSTON 16, MASS.

COmmonwealth 6 - 6318

1950 flier advertising Prescott Baston's public speaking services. According to the flier, "His brilliant, instructive lectures abound with artistic insight, unusual information, human interest, and the true tang of Yankee wit and humor."

A Reader's Digest *reprint accompanying a Siesta Coffee Sebastian Miniature was mailed to 1,000 retail store coffee buyers in 1959. The cover reminds the buyer that* Reader's Digest *advertising and adequate stocks result in "Muchos Pesos with Siesta."*

Meanwhile, with the popularity of ballpoint pens established, Baston offered many of his retail figurines as penstands. The conversion was usually accomplished by modifying the mold for the base and inserting a penholder. This was a rather simple modification, and Baston maintained no production records on exactly what design and how many were produced. All we know is that he began the general penstand retail offering in 1958 and gradually withdrew it until 1967 when the offer was dropped.

In 1960, Theron Pritchard, a Chicago detective enthused over Sebastians, proposed a sales agreement. He would open Sebastian dealerships and warehouse a small inventory in Chicago. Pritchard ordered a few thousand labels similar in appearance to the Marblehead labels, with the wording changed to:

SEBASTIAN MINIATURES
10801 South Peoria St.
Chicago 43, IL

Sales were never brisk during the years Pritchard sold to stores, but increasing numbers of that label are now appearing in Sebastian collector events. More important, Pritchard was largely responsible for obtaining the Chicago St. Jude, Pope John XXIII and Tony Piet-Bunky Knudsen commissions.

In 1963, Baston again joined forces with the Schmid gift distribution forces after a separation of thirteen years. The Boston company was deeply involved with Goebel, the producers of the M. I. Hummel figurines in Germany. Following negotiations between Baston, Schmid and Goebel, Baston designed ten figures in large scale to be fired into ceramicware in Germany and distributed worldwide. He sculpted and painted Henry VIII and Anne Boleyn, David and Dora Copperfield, Tom Sawyer and Aunt Polly ("Mending Time") and a grouping of a Colonial family. After a few sets of the four groupings were fired, both parties decided against further collaboration. The pieces now exist in private collections and are revered as tangible evidence of the momentary collaboration of the great German and American figurine producers.

Baston also created three Toby Jug designs of Washington, Lincoln and John F. Kennedy and two miniature Toby Jugs of John and Jackie Kennedy to serve as small measuring cups. The November 22 shots in Dallas ended any interest in the project and it was summarily dropped.

In 1965, Pope Paul VI visited New York, the first pope to set foot on American soil. Baston designed an "active, traveling Pope Paul" figurine and sold it for several years, primarily through religious gift stores. In 1967, Stanley Home Products in Easthampton, Massachusetts, commissioned Baston to design a baby with a "baby piano" that would be cast and fired into porcelain ceramic overseas and distributed as a music box through the Stanley Home parties. In all, 25,000 boxes were sold.

A Jell-O Cow milk pitcher he had designed was fired in Japan and offered as a cereal milk pitcher for $1.00 and a coupon from national Jell-O ads. Actually, all of these designs for materials other than Ceramastone are not significant in the Sebastian Miniature collection and are treasured today as oddities and memorabilia. His later work in pewter would take a different direction.

In 1967, two events occurred which are of interest to today's collectors. Baston received a commission to design and produce 150 "Doc Berrys" for the good doctor's birthday. The design would later be the focus of a great deal of publicity in the 1980's collector market. The second event was the second and final separation between Baston and Schmid. The companies had been together a total of nine years and had produced much good work together. Following this, design, production and sales activities of Sebastian Miniatures declined steadily while Baston devoted more and more time to commissions produced in pewter.

It is interesting and worthwhile at this stage of the narrative history to summarize Sebastian Miniature design up to this time.

The following tables are only cold numbers, but they do cast light on trends within the long Sebastian history.

Number of Original Sebastian Miniature Designs (SML's)

Period	Designs	Approximate Average per Year
1939-1941 Getting Started	40	13
1942-1945 World War II	7	2
1946-1950 Marblehead Retail	116	23
1951-1959 Marblehead Commercial—I	147	17
1960-1968 Marblehead Commercial—II	51	6
1969-1975 Pewter Years	5	1

Retail SML's versus Commercial

	Retail	Commercial
1939-1950	147	18
1951-1968	61	137
1969-1975	5	0

The large bulge in total designs from 1946 to 1959 is an accurate reflection of studio activities. The striking shift from retail to commercial designs in 1951 is an accurate indication of the shift in volume direction.

Following 1968, only five original designs were added to the Arlington-Marblehead output of 368 designs. The great bulk of the pre-Lance Collection had been formed and distributed.

Pewter Years
1969–1975

In 1968, Ray Kennedy, president of the young Lance Corporation in Hudson, Massachusetts, was searching for original art to cast into pewter figurines. His tiny foundry had been casting precision metal components used by the aerospace and computer industries in the Boston area. Casting the old noble metal into the shape of figurines and sculpture was a new idea and Kennedy wanted to insure good design to give the idea a chance.

One day he spotted a Shawmut Indian owned by a friend and was told that it had been sculpted by an artist in Marblehead. Kennedy called Baston and received permission to cast a prototype sample of the Indian in fine pewter. Baston agreed, and when he saw the results he was extremely pleased with the technical accuracy and appearance. In 1969, Baston signed a contract with Lance assigning several Sebastian designs to Hudson Pewter, Lance's giftware tradename.

In 1969, Lance produced pewter figurines of Baston's newly-produced Concord and Lexington Minutemen and 1951's Christopher Columbus. They were mounted on a wooden base and distributed nationally. From 1970 to 1972, Baston modified ten of his original designs and added three new designs. The modifications were slight, made only so that the gray pewter would still show significant detail.

In 1973, he designed the Hudson American Independence pewter plate depicting events tied to the American Revolution. The Bicentennial celebration was approaching and Americans were beginning to search for durable commemoratives of the occasion. Altogether, Lance sold tens of thousands of these Baston-Hudson Pewter figurines and over 18,000 American Independence plates.

Lance also cast fine pewter sculpture and plates for Royal Worcester, the British porcelain producer. All Lance-manufactured products were labeled "Worcester Pewter." In 1971, Baston, Lance and Worcester planned a Bicentennial commemorative plate series, one plate per year up to 1976. The edition was limited to 10,000 plates and was sold in the finest stores and galleries in America. Plate one, The Boston Tea Party, was an immediate sell-out, as were the four plates that followed. The series now resides in the Bradford Plate Hall of Fame of America's most important collector plates.

Two series of Colonial sculptures and Currier & Ives plates followed these successes, as did a number of additional Hudson projects. Most of this pewter production is still not important to today's Sebastian collectors, but the three following transitions occurring during this period are important.

First, with Sebastian activities already in decline by 1969, added to by the demands of pewter design and production, almost all important production ceased in Marblehead. No new commercial commissions had been accepted and the number of dealers actively promoting Sebastians had dwindled to less than one hundred, most in the Boston area.

Second, a strong and good relationship had developed between Baston and Kennedy, a relationship that allowed for a great deal of trust in cooperative efforts.

Third, by 1975, the Lance Corporation had grown from a tiny castings laboratory to a relatively important factor in the American gift industry. Lance also had plenty of evidence that Baston's work was popular with the buying public.

The stage was set and all the important components had been gathered for what was to occur in the next few years.

America Discovers a Collectible
1976–Present

The America of 1976 had changed as much since 1946 as the change from 1930 to 1946. This degree of change was also obvious in the hobby of collecting.

Beginning in the late 1960's, American business had begun to focus on man's desire to acquire and collect objects. In retrospect, the desire had always been there, but for the first time objects were being produced to be collected. This had never happened before. Throughout man's history, people had saved and displayed objects in a highly personal, rather haphazard and unorganized manner. Stamps and coins were the glaring exceptions, and even they had been organized only a few decades prior. With the production and promotion of these objects, specialty collectibles books such as the one you are reading attracted and turned-on readers who had not even considered themselves collectors before. The number of collector clubs and specialty newsletters began to grow and auction prices rose as the number of collectors looking for rare things grew.

The country had become fascinated with miniature scale. We had been building model trains since the 1930's, but now the layouts became very complex and expensive and scale had shrunk from "O" to "HO" to "N." Dollhouses that were once little girls' toys had become 1:12 scale architectural achievements for their mothers and fathers.

Appreciation for handmade objects was latent following the excesses of mass production and the impersonal Machine Age, but now "Arts and Crafts" and "Organic" had become a necessity for some tastes.

An increase in nostalgia, a harking back to the "good old days," became manifestly obvious. Although oversimplified, we can sympathize with a strong yearning for a pre-nuclear, pre-TV, pre-computer, pre-future shock culture that at least seemed simpler.

Patriotism, following the Vietnam horrors of the Sixties and Watergate revelations of the early Seventies, became vogue again. A search of the day's newspapers indicates no embarrassment or scorn associated with our Bicentennial celebration.

Associated with this was a growing awareness of "Made in America" as a positive attribute. Isolationist before World War II and the domineering world power for twenty years after, we Americans were ill-prepared for the foreign assaults on our automotive industry and our petroleum refineries specifically and American craftsmanship in general.

In the midst of all this, Lance took over production and distribution of Sebastian Miniatures. As we have seen, this line had been relatively inactive since about 1959, seventeen years before. Based on conversations and surveys with thousands of current collectors, no more than 250 persons owned a significant collection of Sebastians in 1976, if that many.

Further, Lance decided to produce 94 of the old Sebastians and distribute them as giftware along with its Hudson Pewter. No one at Lance knew anything about the more than 270 designs they had decided not to produce. Their only interest was in producing attractive and colorful Godey Children, Madonnas, Dickens characters and so on.

Lance began by selecting the 94 designs Baston felt had been the most popular retail sellers over the years. A small production facility was set-up in a small rented building at Kane Industrial Park, a few miles south of the Lance pewter foundry. A converted bakery truck was used to deliver the day's castings to home painters.

A small color brochure was designed and three sales organizations in Boston, New York and Pennsylvania were trained to place the figurines in gift shops. Small ads were placed in gift magazines.

Beginning in 1976, Baston spent at least two days every week instructing the new mold makers, casters and painters in Hudson. He also began making a few personal appearances in some stores in the Boston area that were carryovers from his Marblehead business.

Production and sales progressed slowly in these first years. Demand for Sebastians was low, and most of the public was totally unfamiliar with the little painted figures and the forty years of history behind them. An early Bicentennial sales spurt was followed by a slow and uneventful 1977. In an attempt to arouse interest in the then-booming limited edition marketplace, Lance marketers announced that Captain John Parker, the

This 1976 Brochure lists the 94 Sebastians originally produced and distributed by Lance.

Lexington Minuteman, would be permanently discontinued on October 31, 1977, the last day of Lance's fiscal year. Nobody noticed, and Sebastian Miniature's first "limited edition" passed into history without as much as a ripple on the sales curve. In July, 1977, the Godey Children, Nursery Rhymes and some of the early regional themes that had been discontinued a year-and-a-half earlier were put back into production.

By the middle of 1978, several factors important to the later discovery of Sebastians as collectibles were in place.

Production, after thirty months, was running smoothly in Hudson. Following the marketing tests in New England, New York and Pennsylvania, Lance's distribution organization had been trained for a national introduction in July.

In July, 1977, the author had published a booklet "The Sebastian Story and Chronology." When Lance had taken over distribution, the relatively small number of Sebastian collectors had transferred their questions from Baston to Lance headquarters. Working with Baston's old copyright records, Lance hastily compiled a chronological listing of 283 designs. The Chronology, although woefully inadequate, served a few useful purposes. It told the public that Sebastians had a past, a forty-year record of variety and remarkable continuity. It also warned us that there was much more out there than we had ever guessed. Both collectors and new discoverers kept informing us they had such-and-such a piece and it was not included in our little booklet. We began warming to the task.

Finally, in preparation for July, 1978, Lance and Baston had planned a real limited edition. He had designed Sidewalk Days, a boy and girl on roller skates, in 1938, the year of the Shaker pieces, but had never produced them. Pulling the old masters out of the vault, Lance prepared to issue them as numbered and limited to 10,000 pairs.

In February, 1978, a vicious hurricane snowstorm had destroyed Rockport's Motif No. 1, the old fishing shack reputed to be "the most painted scene in America." Baston was asked to help raise funds for its restoration by the Rockport Artist's League. Baston and Lance planned a limited edition plate, the first

Sebastian Miniature collectors plate ever, combining Baston's colorful painted sculpture center and Lance's pewter rim.

Both of these issues, along with Paul Bunyan, the next design to be permanently retired October 31, were brought to the annual National Collectors Convention in South Bend, Indiana. The combination of the limited editions plus the conscious announcement of Sebastian's long and varied history created a collectibles market sensation.

The rest of 1978 and 1979 were spent with Baston touring the country making personal appearances, national dealers lining up to place orders and production expanded to a new plant in Lee, New Hampshire and a painting facility on Martha's Vineyard to handle the growing backlog.

By the middle of 1979, it was obvious that the American public was in the process of discovering a new collectible, new to them but attractively old in time and wide in intricate variety. Returning to the opening comments in this section, the Sebastians were miniature, with fascinating detail in such current pieces as the Madonnas, Candy Store, Shoemaker and Doctor and wonderful surprises in store with the old St. Joan, Jell-O Woman in the Shoe and Jude Thaddeus.

All of the figurines were obviously handmade. The range of colors on a single design made it obvious that people, not machines, were producing Sebastians.

Almost all Sebastians "look back" to the nostalgic past. Whether in the costumes of the Godey Children, the Family series or Colonial subjects, none of the Sebastians are mirrors of today's pop culture.

Sebastians are openly proud of their American identity. Uncle Sam, Betsy Ross and the presidents are not marred by resentful cynicism. The Victorian characters are satisfied with their age. The Families celebrate their values and are at peace with each other. The Boy Scouts and Campfire Girls look forward to positive lives.

And the design, production and designer are all-American. The Dickens and Shakespearean series stray, but the Mark Twains, Nathaniel Hawthornes, Washington Irvings and nursery rhymes are pure grade school America. There can be no confusion that Sebastian Miniatures are anything but American.

At the same time, it had become obvious that these growing number of collectors demanded and deserved more detailed information on their new interest. Beginning in July, Baston, Marjorie and Woody began scouring the Marblehead studio and files for old designs and written records. By October, 411 Sebastians had been assembled, lined up on shelves in the Studio basement. The Shaker pair was on the upper left shelf and the recently-issued Snow Days on the lower right. With Baston dictating his memories to a secretary, all designs were described and photographed, one-by-one. The result, the *Sebastian Miniatures Collectors Guide*, was published four months later.

At the same time, it was also obvious from the staggering numbers of inquiries on the collection being sent to Lance headquarters that a formal system of information gathering and disseminating was required. Lance and Baston formed the Sebastian Collectors Society, consisting of the author, Membership Director Judy Wilson, Mr. Baston's sharp memory, a typewriter, phone, printing press and computer. The first newsletter was published in February and mailed to the Society's 1,300 members.

Meanwhile, Baston had resumed his Sebastian design activities. Following Sidewalk Days and the Motif No. 1 plate, he quickly followed with Family Sing, Mt. Rushmore, two new Godey children, Building Days, Family Picnic and Snow Days. He also pursued a frenetic national personal appearance schedule. A look at his 1979 schedule of appearances is revealing:

January	Atlantic City, New Jersey	**August**	Chicago, Illinois
April	Thousand Oaks, California	**September**	Burlington, Massachusetts
	San Francisco, California	**October**	Englewood, New Jersey
	San Jose, California	**November**	Niles, Ohio
	Kennewick, Washington		Milwaukee, Wisconsin
	Aberdeen, Washington		Kansas City, Missouri
	Braintree, Massachusetts		Des Moine, Iowa
	Fort Wayne, Indiana		Orlando, Florida
	Dayton, Ohio		Springfield, Massachusetts
May	Louisville, Kentucky		Quincy, Massachusetts
	Atlanta, Georgia	**December**	Pomona, California
	Scotch Plains, New Jersey		Los Angeles, California
	Garden City, New York		San Diego, California
	Pittsburgh, Pennsylvania		Houston, Texas
	State College, Pennsylvania		
	Wilkes Barre, Pennsylvania		
July	South Bend, Indiana		

Prescott Baston and Woody together in Woody's Wayland home. The craft continues.

Prescott Baston's Marblehead studio at 13 Basset Street, the scene of the creation of the Sebastian Collection.

In all, this schedule represented appearance in 31 cities in 17 states in one year, not to mention the banquets, television and radio shows and endless waits in airports and motels. With this schedule, his design work and production assistance, it was obvious that Prescott Baston was, as mentioned in the beginning of this history, as active as he had ever been!

Meanwhile, the publishing of the *Collectors Guide* was followed by a confusing but interesting situation. Established collectors and aftermarket dealers informed us the Sebastians had "gone underground." Old pieces had simply disappeared from flea markets, antique shops and antique auctions. Then, according to the same people, the pieces had reappeared, commanding prices of a hundred dollars and more compared to the previous ten dollars. The *Guide* had put the collection in historical perspective. National exposure and the publicity resulting from the personal appearances had greatly increased the number of serious collectors searching for antique specialties.

A Boston auctioneeer, familiar with Sebastians and their rise in prices over the past half year, conducted an all-Sebastian auction in September. The results were staggering to Baston, old collectors and new. A total of 350 collectors from seventeen states paid $19,000 for 90 rare Sebastians. The high price was $1,600 for a sales sample kit Baston had used in the Fifties to sell three Shakespearean couples. Low price was $50 for a Little Mother with a Marblehead label. Paul Bunyan, discontinued only two years earlier, sold for $325 and the Clown, discontinued a year earlier, $225. The Jell-O Scottish Lass was auctioned at $400, Mr. Sheraton at $500, Jell-O Moose at $525 and the John F. Kennedy Toby Jug at $550. The average sales was over $200!

News of the auction was reported in the *Boston Globe* and the results were picked up by collector newspapers, magazines, dealers and collectors all over the country.

In September, 1981, Prescott's son "Woody" introduced his first Sebastian Miniature, First Kite. The event was the final outcome of Prescott wanting him to design Sebastians but afraid to push him into it and Woody wanting to design Sebastians but afraid to steal any attention from his father.

Woody began working part-time in the Marblehead Studio during junior high school (1958–1960). He spent vacations mold-making, casting, cleaning and painting. Following four years of study at Boston University, he graduated in 1968 with a Bachelor of Fine Arts degree, majoring in sculpture. He helped make Sebastians during all these years.

Woody joined the Army following graduation and, after Officer Candidate School, served as a Security Officer in Zelo, a small northern Italian town halfway between Florence and Venice. His father had strengthened his ties with Lance by 1971, the year of Woody's discharge, and Lance hired Woody as its production manager for pewter.

In the summer of 1975, Woody had once again become involved with the Sebastian Miniatures of his youth. He and his father planned for the closing down of production in Marblehead and the startup of production in Hudson.

Woody married Margery Flowers in June, 1973, and they have a son, Prescott W. Baston III. The piano in Woody's Wayland home is the piano in Family Sing as is the wood stove in Family Reads Aloud.

Woody has had to relearn some of his sculptural training to sculpt Sebastians. "My father has always used a special technique in his sculpting that has given Sebastians a particular appearance. Actually, modelling clays are now available that are hard enough to allow final detailing, but when I used them they just didn't look right. The extra steps, from clay to hydrocal to final detail carving, gives my work the Sebastian look."

With the introduction of Woody Baston as the heir to the conscience of the Sebastian Collection, we have come to the end of this narrative history. The events of the past two years are too fast and too fresh and the author's involvement with them has been too close to allow any more "history." We are not in history now. We are in the present, a confusing swirl of questions, answers, decisions, events and demands. We are still with our Doc Berrys, School Days, limited editions, new designs, auctions, *Value Registers*, newsletters, festivals, seminars, sales quotas and collector inquiries. It is refreshing and encouraging, however, to be able to conclude this history with the same optimistic words we used over two years ago in the first *Guide:*

"And this is only the beginning. Only now are Americans, previously unfamiliar with the Sebastian story, beginning to discover and collect this over-forty-year-old expression of a man's life. The future is unpredictable in terms of the extent to which Sebastian Miniatures will become part and parcel of our American heritage.

"Prescott Baston is alive and well, embarked on yet another stage of his career. The old established collectors, to a person, are pleased with the national acceptance of work they have so long cherished. As of this writing, authorized dealerships are coming aboard daily, intrigued by the groundswell of this collecting event.

"It would seem, in retrospect, that a whole new dimension has been added to a philosophy penned by Prescott Baston in 1948." "Two goals have guided my work through the years. First, to do the most honest portrayals I can. Second to create scenes so appealing that other people immediately experience a sense of pleasure from them!"

SEBASTIAN MINIATURE DESIGN AND PRODUCTION

Prescott Baston and a group of moldmakers, casters, cleaners, costume painters and feature painters produced Sebastian Miniatures in his Arlington basement and Marblehead studio from 1938 to 1975. Lance production began in Hudson in 1976, spread to Martha's Vineyard in 1978 and Lee, New Hampshire in 1979. Now all Sebastians are designed in the old Marblehead studio, with moldmaking in Hudson and production in Lee. The design technique, mold process and production technique are the same today as with the first production runs.

In this pictorial essay, we will trace a Sebastian Miniature from its beginning in Marblehead to the final steps in Lee.

Step 1: Baston begins with an idea. Sometimes the idea is a request from Lance marketing ("We need a new Children's Pair. How about two children in school?") Sometimes the request is from a customer ("Can you do a Mt. Rushmore?") Sometimes the idea springs from something Baston wants to do ("I want a Godey brother and sister.") Wherever the source, all composition, costuming and coloring is pure Baston.

Baston is portrayed here working on an armature (a wire that will form the "skeleton" of the work). After all the research is completed, Baston works on the basic composition of the individual or the scene. He adds clay to the armature and the new miniature grows in mass.

Step 2: When all the clay has been added to the armature, Baston begins preliminary detailing. Heads, arms and legs take shape and in this instance, the beginnings of a rifle. An open book at the left reveals costume details. Godey models are perched on the upper left and sculpting tools lie behind his right arm.

Step 3: Baston uses a sculpting technique called the "lost mold" process. In preparing his first mold, he inserts thin metal fins in his soft clay. They will provide parting lines after the mold has been formed. Here he works on the "Skipping Rope" Godey child (SML 373).

Step 4: Baston spreads a coat of blue liquid plaster over the finned clay. The blue wil be used in Step 10 of the modeling procedure.

Step 5: Baston applies from two to four coats of white plaster over the blue coat. The rough mold becomes stronger as each coat is added.

Step 6: When the mold has hardened, Baston pulls it off the original clay, the mold separating at the fins. This creates a mirror-image cavity and destroys the original clay.

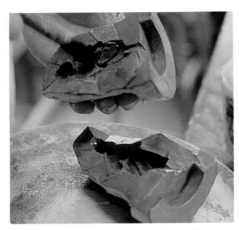

Step 7: Baston then applies a chemical release agent that activates the blue color lining the interior of the plaster mold.

Step 8: Baston straps the mold segments to form a hollow cavity.

Step 9: Liquid Ceramastone is poured into the mold cavity until the mold is brim full. The liquid hardens until the master mold and the Ceramastone inside are one solid mass, separated from each other only by the blue agent.

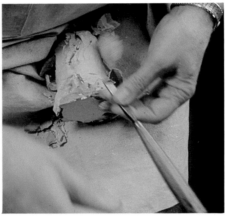

Step 10: Baston chips away the outer master mold, therefore, the term "lost mold process." When he gets to the blue layer, he knows he is close to the figurine inside. The result of all ten steps thus far is a rough, slightly oversized Sebastian Miniature.

Step 11: Working with this rough casting and sharp tools, Baston carves final detail into the miniature. The Marblehead artist spends a great deal of time on this detail (buttons, cheekbones, drapes, fingers, etc.), probably the outstanding characteristic of Sebastian Miniatures. This step completes the modeling process.

Step 12: Baston applies a thick rubber coat to the final detailed miniature. The rubber is a special mixture, rigid enough to capture and hold the original detail and yet pliable enough to be used over and over again.

This production mold is then transferred to the studio at Lee, New Hampshire for the final five steps in production.

Step 13: A caster pours liquid Ceramastone into the mold cavity. When necessary for structural support, wires are inserted into the mold before pouring. Over half of all Sebastian Miniatures have wires inside them for strength.

Step 14: When the Ceramastone has hardened it is removed from the rubber mold. Every miniature is then hand cleaned with a knife to remove any excess material. In this photo, a parting line (where the two mold sides come together) is removed from the chair in "Self-Portrait."

Step 15: "Costume painting," or the painting of all the large areas, is done by a trained group of home painters in the Lee area. A painter will come in at a special time and receive a kit from the supervisor consisting of 20 to 30 white miniatures and four to five bottles of paint for that particular assignment. When she has completed the kit, she will return it to the studio and receive another kit. Here a painter applies an earth tan to Doc Berry's shirt.

Baston has always used home painters, dating from the earliest days in Arlington. This process is a return to New England's pioneering "cottage industry." Training at the studio for home painters is constant, as is the flow of home painters during the day in the Kitting Room.

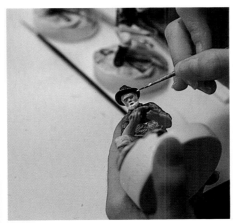

Step 16: Micro-miniature features (eyes, lips, eyebrows, etc.) are one of the distinctive trademarks of Sebastian Miniatures. All featuring is done in the studio by skilled painters using brushes with just a few hairs. Of all the crafts aside from modelling, featuring is the most skilled. During rushes in the Marblehead days, Baston would do most of the featuring himself. Half of the painted Shawmut Indians were featured by Baston.

Here a feature painter applies eyebrows to the Forty-niner.

Step 17: In this final step, a fine coat of sealant is applied with a spray gun. In addition to this coat, each base is hand-dipped, sealing the costume painter's initials.

The miniature is now ready for packaging and shipment to authorized dealers across the country. All processes and materials are the same as used by Baston in Marblehead during the 1950's. Baston himself spends at least one day a week in Lee and continually runs spot checks on all production.

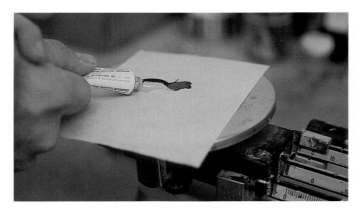

COLOR PREPARATION

Color is a vital ingredient in the preparation of Sebastian Miniatures. Baston has built a color library of 88 distinct colors, shades and hues. "1847 Red" is the particular red he used on his R. H. Stearns Couple in 1947, while "Manger Yellow" is a special yellow. The recipes for each color are registered in terms of grams of different colors and ounces of water. All colors are specially prepared and shelved for distribution to home painters.

The poster display on the right illustrates about half of the 88 colors.

Beginning in May, 1981, Sebastian studios have been open to the public during working hours. A simple call a few days before your visit will ensure a warm welcome and 30-minute tour of all facilities.

Lee is located a few miles from Durham, campus of the University of New Hampshire and about an hour north of Boston.

COLLECTING TIPS AND TERMINOLOGY

─── CLASSIFICATION ───

A thorough system of classification has been assigned to every Sebastian Miniature design. This system is explained with the most complex listing, the Shoemaker.		SML 292-C (*Haverhill Penstand*) SML 292-D (*Plain Figurine Base*)	292-C C 1960 1,000 292-D SR 1962–1975 LR 1976–Present (No. 6217)
SML 292 Shoemaker (*Nat'l Bank of Plymouth, Plymouth County*)	1958 292 C 1958 400	SML 292-E (*First County National Bank*)	292-E C 1962 250
SML 292-A (*National Bank of Plymouth, Brockton*)	292-A C 1958 250	SML 292-F (*International Shoe-Rand Penstand*)	292-F C 1963 100
SML 292-B (*Paperweight*)	292-B SR 1959–1962	SML 292-G (*International Shoe-Ewing Penstand*)	292-G C 1963 100

SML 292: The original design.

SML 292-A: The first variation from the original, usually an inscription permanently cast into the base or a color variation of the figurine itself, always in quantities over 100 for a particular purpose. In this case, the wording on the base added the word "Brockton" to the original "National Bank of Plymouth County."

SML 292-B: A "paperweight" design indicates retail sales with no commercial wording.

SML 292-C: A Shoemaker design on a "Haverhill" penstand base.

SML 292-D: A Shoemaker design on a plain figurine base indicates a design for retail sales with (a) no penstand, (b) no paperweight and (c)

no commercial inscription on base.

SML 292-F: A Shoemaker design on a penstand base inscribed "International Shoe-Rand."

The right hand system describes the year of original design (1958) and the commercial status by year and quantity of each issue of that design.

292 C 1958 400: 400 pieces of the Commercial National Bank of Plymouth County base were issued in 1958.

292-B SR 1959–1962: The paperweight version of the design was sold through Sebastian Retail stores from 1959 to 1962.

292-D SR 1962–1974
LR 1976–Present
(No. 6217)

The plain figurine base version of the design was sold through Sebastian Retail stores from 1962 to 1975. Then the design was continued by Lance up to the present time and is available through authorized dealers as Model No. 6217.

A typical listing is:

SML 301 Siesta Coffee Penstand
1959 C 1959 1,000

SML 301 is the 301st Sebastian Miniature design. The Siesta Coffee penstand, designed in 1959, was a Commercial job with 1,000 penstands issued in 1959.

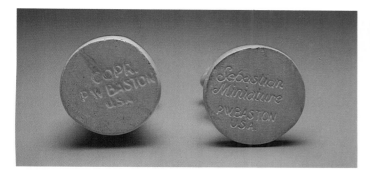

LABELS

Many Sebastian Miniatures were produced from 1946 to the present. Labels and permanent painter signatures have become a convenient method of determining the years of production and, hence, of approximate rarity. The following are helpful tips in determining the age of a Sebastian Miniature.

1. Arlington vs. Marblehead (1938–1945 vs. 1946–1975)

When Baston began producing Sebastians, he produced in relatively small quantities. The quantities were so small that he could imprint a "COPR. P. W. BASTON U.S.A." with a stamp in the base while the liquid material was hardening. The stamp had to be applied when the Ceramastone was hard enough to "remember" the imprint, and still wet enough to accept it. This method was obviously impossible with higher production runs.

In 1939, Baston changed his imprint to "Sebastian Miniatures P. W. BASTON, U.S.A." Carbone had him remove all identification after 1940, so both imprints are quite rare.

Many Arlington pieces appear with no imprint or label. Since many of the Early Pair Series were produced into 1958, there is no way of identifying Arlington vs. Marblehead production with these pieces.

2. Marblehead vs. Lance

Baston had designed and produced 368 designs and 192 variations (a total of 560 collectible miniatures) from 1938 through 1975. Since that time, Lance has continued production on 133 of those variations, or less than one-quarter. Therefore, identification of Marblehead vs. Lance is not a problem with 427 designs and variations. All production on them ceased when Lance entered the picture. It is with the 133 continued designs that an identification problem exists.

Baston attached a silver-green label (left in the photo) to the base of his Marblehead-produced pieces. If that label on an old piece is still affixed, that means it is a "Marblehead Piece," or rare.

3. Lance Production

When Lance began production in January, 1976, it affixed a four-digit blue-on-white label on the base. Lance continued this practice until May, 1976, when the company added a white-copy on lime-green paper label (third from left)

that said "Sebastian Miniatures, Hudson, Mass." Then, in November, the company replaced the white-lime green label with a black-copy on dark green paper label (fourth from left). This was used until the end of December, 1978.

In 1979, the company used a pastel blue label, 1980 a yellow label and 1981 a red label. In 1982, a purple label is being used. Also, painters were required to sign their initials, the year of painting and the location of painting on the base beginning in 1979.

A: 1979   1: Lee, New Hampshire
B: 1980   2: Hudson, Massachusetts
C: 1981   3: Martha's Vineyard, Massachusetts

Thus, a blue label marked JP/A/2 meant that Joan Priest painted that miniature in 1979 in Hudson. Production in Martha's Vineyard stopped in 1980 and in Hudson in early 1981. Now all miniatures are made in Lee.

Here are tips on identifying years of production:

SML 163 Phoebe (Unmarked)

Phoebe was produced from 1950–1975 for the retail line. Since Lance did not continue production, it *had* to be Marblehead, whether it had a Marblehead label or not.

SML 277 Colonial Glassblower (Marblehead Label)

The label certifies the miniature is produced from 1957 to 1975 and is a rare Marblehead piece.

SML 277 Colonial Glassblower (Yellow Label)

Produced in 1980.

SML 277 Colonial Glassblower (*No label, but marked DM/B/1 on base in pencil*)

Produced in 1980.

SML 277 Colonial Glassblower (*No label, no marking*)

This is the worst condition for classification and the *only* area where identification is a problem. The piece could be Marblehead and could be 1976–1978 with the label off in both cases. It *could not* be 1979 on, since the pencil marking would be obvious. In all cases of this one type, the piece should be brought to a Certified Sebastian Appraiser for final judgment.

C: Commercial designs, produced on contract for one company or gift store and not offered through Baston's retail stores. Well-known examples include the Jell-O series, the Johnson & Johnson series and the *Reader's Digest* rebates. Commercial designs represent approximately one-third of all designs and, until 1975, approximately three-quarters of all Marblehead production.

Ceramastone: A trade name for the material used in casting Sebastian Miniatures; fine-ground gypsum cement particles in liquid suspension that harden to a chalky white after about five minutes of set-time.

After World War II, Baston was encouraged to cast his work in fired ceramic but he refused. Following the lead of artist John Rogers (see Rogers Groups, SML 193), he wanted to keep the price of his work within the reach of many.

Chicago Label: Theron Pritchard, a Marblehead policeman and Sebastian enthusiast, moved to Chicago in 1960. With Baston's cooperation, he began selling Sebastian Miniatures to dealers in the Chicago area. From 1962 to 1965 all Sebastians for orders he took bore a silver-green Marblehead label with the words:

    Sebastian Miniatures
    10801 So. Peoria St.
    Chicago 43, Ill.

In addition, Pritchard was responsible for the St. Jude, Pope John XXIII and Tony Piet-Bunky Knudsen commissions.

Collectors Society: A group formed of Sebastian Studios, dealers and collectors, headquartered in Hudson, Massachusetts, offering a quarterly newsletter on new issues, coming events, features on collecting and other information of significant interest to Sebastian collectors. Also a correspondence and phone answering service for individual inquiries. For more information write:

    Sebastian Miniatures Collectors Society
    321 Central Street
    Hudson, Mass. 01749
    (617) 568–1401

Discontinued Piece: The one Marblehead design that is annually discontinued forever on October 31. Past discontinued designs are:

    1977: Lexington Minuteman
    1978: Paul Bunyan
    1979: Clown
    1980: George Washington with Cannon
    1981: Uncle Sam
    1982: Abraham Lincoln

LC: Large Ceramastone. Prescott Baston produced 44 sculptures for commercial sale that were too large to be considered Miniature. All of the pieces were cast in Ceramastone. Each piece has been identified in at least one private collection outside of Baston's studio. These are catalogued on pages 141 to 144.

LR: Lance Retail, designated as those Sebastians produced and distributed nationally after January 1, 1976 by the Lance Corporation in Hudson, Massachusetts. Most important, Lance retail signifies the beginning of the shift of marketing Sebastians as collectible figurines versus Baston's Marblehead high-volume Commercial business and low-volume retail sales.

If Lance still offers the design through its authorized dealers, the Model Number is listed.

Molds: The rubber cavities retaining the original design and used to produce cast copies of the original. Mold life for Sebastian Miniatures is from five-to-ten years before they become too rigid. All mold-making is now done in Hudson, Massachusetts and supervised by Prescott Baston.

One-of-a-Kinds: Baston designed many sculptures and miniatures on speculation or for his own amusement. These "one-ofs" are not listed in this book since they are not nor ever will be available to collectors. Among these are three miniatures listed in the 1980 First Edition Collectors Guide; Babe Ruth, Robin Hood and Little John (Version II) and the Sylvania light display.

Painting Variation

Baston often changed a color on a design. In the case of Savin' Sandy, he changed an entire issue at the request of a commercial buyer. With the Naumkeag Indian, he shifted from a painted to a bronzed version. Applying a single bronze, gold or silver paint, of course, decreased the cost and/or allowed him to produce more pieces in less time.

In many instances, Sebastian collectors own pieces that have colors not listed or illustrated in this Guide. From 1946 until 1975, Baston's retail customers often ordered in small quantities. If, for example, a store ordered 10 "Boy and Pelican" figurines, he may not have produced that particular piece for five years. Rather than keep detailed records on all small-quantity jobs, he would paint that small order by memory. If his memory was not exact, the color would be different. With this ease of variation, no record-keeping was possible or desirable.

Paperweight: A large penstand base without the penstand device attached to it.

Penstand: A Sebastian Miniature cast on a large base containing a holder for a ballpoint

pen. Baston cast his first penstand for the NECCO Company in 1949 (SML 122) and he used them extensively until around 1967. In 1958, parallel with the growing popular usage of ballpoints, he added penstands to many of his retail figurine designs. This lasted until 1967 when the retail business had slowed considerably.

PF: Pewter Figurines. Baston designed 33 figurines that were cast into fine pewter by Hudson and Royal Worcester. These are cataloged on pages 145 to 147.

PP: Pewter Plates. Prescott Baston produced a total of 14 plate designs that were cast into fine pewter for Royal Worcester and Hudson. These designs are catalogued on pages 148 to 150.

SR: Sebastian Retail, designed for sale through gift shops from 1938 to 1975. From 1951 to 1976, the retail line was used more and more to fill-in slow periods between higher volume Commercial contracts. The SR designation ended in December, 1975, before Lance began distributing the miniatures nationally and, more important, began emphasizing retail business over Commercial.

SML: Sebastian Miniature Listing

Every major design (not including base or color variations) is classified in chronological order fom 1938's Shaker Man up to the present designs.

Sebastian Plates

One of the six plates produced by Sebastian Studios since 1978 consisting of a painted bonded porcelain center and a fine pewter rim. These are catalogued on page 140.

Value Register:

A publication of the Sebastian Miniatures Collectors Society that tracks the aftermarket for the consensus values of rare Sebastian Miniatures. Published and brought up-to-date periodically, the Register lists a conservative number for prices being realized at auctions and through secondary market dealers.

Variation:

Baston varied his basic designs by painting or more often, by changing a cast inscription in the base. Only significant variations (more than 100 pieces produced) are listed in this catalog.

SEBASTIAN MINIATURES®

THE SEBASTIAN MINIATURES COLLECTION

Following the successful design and production of the Shaker couple, Baston contracted with Carbone, Inc., 342 Boylston Street, Boston, to design a series of historical couples. Hans Laaby, Carbone president, told Baston, "We can't sell three pair. We need at least a dozen pair for the Boston Gift Show" (*in March, 1939*). Baston produced eight pair, and, with the Shakers, Sebastian Miniatures were introduced to the American public. Eight more pair were introduced a year later (*March, 1940*).

Any of the early couples bearing a Baston copyright in the base were produced from 1938 to 1940. As the line became important to Carbone, they insisted that any identification be removed.

The Shakers, of limited interest, were issued until 1950. The others were converted to two figures on one base in 1958 or discontinued from production.

SML 1 Shaker Man   1938 SR 1938–1950
SML 2 Shaker Lady

The Shakers (see page 11) were Baston's first two miniature designs. Designed and issued in the Spring of 1938, they mark the birth of Sebastian Miniatures.

Sold originally to the Shaker glen House in Woburn, Massachusetts, they were introduced in March, 1939, as Sebastian Miniatures through Carbone, the Boston gift distributor. They were produced until 1950 and then discontinued.

The original Shakers were a celibate sect of Second Adventists, founded in the 18th century in England and transplanted in the U.S. by Ann Lee. Derisively titled "Shakers" from the wild contortions of their religious dances, Shaker settlements existed in New England for a time. They are known best today for the spartan-simple clarity of their architecture and furniture.

The Shaker Glen House restaurant existed until the early 1950's and then closed.

SML 3 George Washington   1939 SR 1939–1958
SML 4 Martha Washington

George and Martha Washington are the first pair of American couples designed by Baston for Carbone.

A gift shop at Mt. Vernon (near Alexandria, Virginia) "bought grosses" of this pair over the years. The pair, along with John Alden and Priscilla and the Williamsburg couple, were the best sellers in the Early Couples series.

The individual figures were merged onto one base (George and Martha Washington, SML 287) in 1958 and remain today in Lance distribution.

SML 5 John Alden   1939 SR 1939–1958
SML 6 Priscilla

In his long narrative poem, "The Courtship of Miles Standish" (1858), Henry Wadsworth Longfellow has Miles Standish, the captain of the original Plymouth (Massachusetts) settlement, send his friend John Alden to woo Priscilla Mullins for him. Despite his honest pleas for the older man, Priscilla prefers John as her husband ("Speak for yourself, John Alden"). When Miles is reported killed, the lovers plan their marriage. On the eve of the wedding, Standish returns to give his blessings to the young couple.

Long a Sebastian favorite, the pair remained "The most popular of the couples" until 1958 when they were mounted on a single base (SML 286). On one singular occasion, Carbone ordered 84 dozen pair, the largest single order prior to the Commercial orders.

Baston, on request from collectors, created a Miles Standish in 1953 by changing Coronado's title on the base (see SML 13).

SML 7 Williamsburg Governor   1939 SR 1939–1958
SML 8 Williamsburg Lady

Baston's aim with his first set of eight historical pairs was to represent all sections of the early United States. Williamsburg, Virginia was settled in 1632, an outgrowth of Jamestown (1607) and paralleling the development of the Massachusetts Bay Colony (1628), itself an outgrowth of Plymouth Plantation (1620).

With restoration (begun in 1926 with the financial support of John D. Rockefeller, Jr.) now complete, the official Williamsburg gift shop purchased hundreds of the Williamsburg Sebastians every year and since the renewal of Sebastian interest in 1976, remains an important Sebastian dealer. The two designs were unified in 1958 to the present Williamsburg Couple (SML 285).

SML 11 Gabriel   1939 SR 1939–1958
SML 12 Evangeline

In *Evangeline, A Tale of Acadie* (1847), a narrative poem by Henry Wadsworth Longfellow, the lovers, Gabriel Lajeunesse and Evangeline Bellefontaine, are separated when the British expel the Acadians from Nova Scotia. He is carried to Louisiana and she to New England. The two spend years looking for one another. Nursing the sick in an epidemic in Philadelphia, she recognizes him as the dying man in her care. Now an old woman, Evangeline also dies and the two are buried together.

This Sebastian pair was never a terribly strong seller and must be listed as rarer than many of the other pairs in the series.

SML 9 Benjamin Franklin   1939 SR 1939–1958
SML 10 Deborah Franklin

Benjamin Franklin (1706–1790) is tied forever with the American Revolution, the Declaration of Independence, the Federal Constitutional Convention, the Franklin stove, bifocal glasses, *Poor Richard's Almanack*, the identification of electricity in lightning and just about everything else typifying the Philadelphia of the late 1700's.

In his Sebastian pair, Baston portrays Deborah with a piece of knitting for one of their many children. Discontinued forever in 1958, this Franklin design has no connection with later Sebastian Franklins.

SML 13 Coronado   1939 (*13–14*) SR 1939–1958
SML 13-A Miles Standish
SML 14 Coronado's Senora   13-A SR 1953–1958

Francisco Vasquez de Coronado (1510–1554), Spanish explorer, reached New Mexico in 1540. From there he journeyed in the Texas panhandle, Oklahoma and Kansas. In 1554, Coronado was dismissed from his governorship of Nueva Galicia in Mexico and lived the rest of his life in obscurity in Mexico City.

In 1953, in response for a Miles Standish to accompany John Alden and Priscilla (SML 5 and 6), Baston inscribed Standish in Coronado's base and outsold the "new" design "five to one" until both were discontinued in 1958. In 1980, Baston mounted the man and woman on one base and introduced them as "Coronado and Senora" (SML 383).

SML 15 Sam Houston   1939 SR 1939–1958
SML 16 Margaret Houston

Sam Houston (1793–1863) became a champion of Texas independence from Mexico. As commander-in-chief of the Texas Army, he decisively defeated General Santa Anna at San Jacinto in 1836 and served as president of the new republic until 1844. He retired as governor of Texas (admitted to the Union in 1845) when, in 1861, he refused to join the Confederacy and secede from the Union.

In 1980, Baston mounted these two designs on one base and introduced them as Margaret and Sam Houston (SML 382).

SML 17 Indian Warrior   1939 (*Without name*) SR 1939–1947
SML 17-A Nanepashemet   (*With names*) SR 1948–1958
SML 18 Indian Maiden
SML 18-A Webcowit

Baston wanted a set of native Americans in his first series of Early Couples. The first designs bore no particular designation other than "Indian Couple."

In 1948, two years after his move to Marblehead, Baston named the two figures after an Indian couple famous in the early Marblehead settlement story.

SML 19 Jean Laffite   1940 SR 1940–1958
SML 20 Catherine Laffite

Jean Lafitte (1780–1826) led a band of privateers and smugglers off the coast of New Orleans to Galveston, Texas. His ships, commissioned by several of the Latin American nations in revolt against Spain, preyed on Spanish commerce.

Refusing an offer to aid the British in their attempt on New Orleans, Laffite and his men assisted Andrew Jackson in the Battle of New Orleans and were pardoned by President Madison.

When several members of his colony attacked American property, the U.S. government dispatched a naval force against him in 1821. He retired peacefully.

Baston portrayed Laffite and Catherine, his native wife.

SML 21 Dan'l Boone   1940 SR 1940–1958
SML 22 Mrs. Dan'l Boone

Baston designed Dan'l Boone and Mrs. Boone in 1940, a full 24 years before Fess Parker brought the frontiersman to national attention (prime-time television in September, 1964 to August, 1970).

The real life Boone (1734–1820), an English Quaker, left Pennsylvania in 1750 and settled (1752) in North Carolina. Mrs. Boone, the former Rebecca Bryan, refused to accompany him to Florida in 1756. In March, 1775, he founded Boonesboro on the Kentucky River and later became much involved in the Revolutionary War.

The Boone pair were relatively popular sellers until the design was discontinued in 1958.

SML 23 Peter Stuyvesant   1940 SR 1940–1958
SML 24 Annie Stuyvesant

Peter Stuyvesant (1610–1672), Dutch director general of New Amsterdam (later New York City) beginning in 1647. Overwhelmed by a surprise English attack, Stuyvesant surrendered New Amsterdam in 1664. He spent the rest of his life on his Manhattan farm and was buried there under his chapel, now the site of a church, St. Mark's-in-the-Bowery.

Baston's first design had nothing to do with his later portrayal of Peter Stuyvesant in 1960 for the Museum of the City of New York (SML 313).

SML 25 John Harvard   1940 SR 1940–1958
SML 26 Mrs. Harvard

John Harvard (1607–1638) was chief founder of Harvard University (named after him in 1638). He immigrated in 1637 from Southwark, England to Charlestown, Massachusetts (then the Massachusetts Bay Colony). He was assistant to the pastor and teaching elder of Charlestown's First Church. He bequeathed £780 (half of his estate) and his library of 320 volumes toward the founding of the new college. This gift immortalized his name in American education.

SML 27 John Smith   1940 SR 1940–1958
SML 28 Pocahontas

Captain John Smith (1580–1631), English explorer, came to Jamestown, Virginia in 1607 and became president of the governing council of the colony. The legend of his rescue from death by Pocahontas is based on his own story, told in his *Generall Historie of Virginia, New England, and the Summer Isles* (1624).

Pocahontas (1595–1617) was the daughter of Powhatan, an Indian chief of Virginia. Following the legend of her rescue of John Smith from her father, she married John Rolfe, a Jamestown colonist, bringing the colonists peace with the Indians. In 1616, baptized under the name of Rebecca, she was brought to England.

Baston's pair remained popular until discontinued in 1958.

SML 29 William Penn   1940 SR 1940–1958
SML 30 Hannah Penn

William Penn (1644–1718) gained a reputation in England for his crusades in favor of religious toleration. In 1682, he journeyed to America where the earliest settlers were already laying out Philadelphia in accordance with his earlier planning. The early history of Pennsylvania is thoroughly influenced by his liberal and freedom-oriented principles.

Baston portrayed Penn with his wife, Hannah. Governor Penn holds the royal charter to the Colony.

SML 31 Buffalo Bill   1940 SR 1940–1958
SML 32 Annie Oakley

Buffalo Bill's Wild West Show featured this pair from 1885 to 1902.

William Frederick Cody (1846–1917), born near Davenport, Iowa, was an American plainsman, scout and showman. His adventures with the Pony Express, as an army scout and a buffalo hunter were the basis for later stories told about him. In 1883 he organized his Show and toured with it throughout the United States and Europe.

Annie Oakley (1860–1926), original name Phoebe Anne Oakley Mozee, was an expert marksman from childhood on. She was a major attraction of Buffalo Bill's Show where she performed remarkable feats of markmanship. She died in 1926 when Prescott Baston was 17 years old.

In 1980, Baston mounted these two designs on one base and issued them as Buffalo Bill and Annie Oakley (SML 384).

SML 33 James Monroe   1940 SR 1940–1958
SML 34 Elizabeth Monroe

President James Monroe (1758–1831) was sixth president of the United States and declarer of the Monroe Doctrine (1823). The Doctrine states that the U.S. will not permit Europe to extend its political system to the Western hemisphere.

Portrayed with his wife, Elizabeth, the Monroe pair concluded Baston's rapid design activity to establish Sebastian Miniatures as a retail line distributed by Carbone. The next several years (1941 to 1945) would be occupied by production, a few designs and the dominating World War II duties.

SML 35 Rooster   1941 SR 1941
SML 36 Ducklings
SML 37 Peacock
SML 38 Doves
SML 39 Pheasant
SML 40 Swan

With his Shakers and Early Couples underway, the period 1941 through 1945 marked a five-year period of design experimentation. Later designs would continue history and Americana, plus Baston's literary figures. In 1941, prior to the Japanese attack on Pearl Harbor and U.S. entry into World War II, Carbone asked Baston to design a set of figurines depicting birds.

"I was never at ease with the subject matter and nothing ever came of my designs. These six were on the market briefly but they had nothing to commend them. They were like so many other European imports. I made a few and then called it quits." (Left to right: Rooster, unpainted Ducklings, Peacock and Pheasant. The Doves and Swan are unavailable for photography.)

SML 41 Secrets   1941 SR 1941
SML 41-A Kitten

Baston designed a pair of cats mounted on a base inscribed "Secrets." He created a mold of only one kitten and issued that as a single figure. As with his birds (SML 35), he was dissatisfied with this work and produced only two dozen sets.

SML 42 Majorette   1942 SR 1942
SML 43 Cymbals
SML 44 Horn
SML 45 Tuba
SML 46 Drum
SML 47 Accordion

In 1942, Carbone, the Boston gift distributor, was unable to import its European lines because of the war. One popular line of figurines that were especially missed were a group of six children in a band, made of wood by a German manufacturer before the war. At Carbone's request, Baston designed Ceramastone figurines that looked like the German wooden pieces. This accounts for the uncharacteristic appearance of these Sebastian Miniatures.

Baston produced 200 sets of the Band for the 1942 Christmas season but the designs never caught on. "They didn't look like Sebastians."

SML 48 Raphael's Madonna of   1943 SR 1943
         Chair Christmas Ornament

Almost as an accidental prelude to Baston's 1951 Raphael Madonna figurines (SML 169, 170 and 171), he designed this Christmas ornament in 1943. Portraying in bas relief the Madonna of Chair (Raphael's painting, now in the Pitti Palace, Florence, Italy), the 1-1/4″ diameter disc has a small wire loop cast into the Ceramastone.

Conceived and issued in a time long before the serious collection of Christmas ornaments, the discs were priced at two dollars and were considered far too expensive. Baston made only 25 for Carbone's "market test" and then the project was stopped.

The year 1946 marked a dramatic change in Sebastian Miniatures. The war was over and Prescott Baston moved from his Arlington basement to his new studio in Marblehead. In addition to distribution with Carbone, he was developing "Folks in Little" with Schmid Bros. In addition to the Early Couples (SML 3 to 34), he was developing new series for Carbone. In addition to these two retail efforts, Baston accepted his first real Commercial commission from the Puritan Candy Company (the Colonial Spinner), a direction leading to 1947's Shawmut Indian and the promise of large production runs that were eventually to dominate the 1950's and 1960's.

Baston's first series for Carbone was his Dickens designs. Shown here as a group, the collection grew until a base was designed in 1966 to display all elements.

Patent Pending

Baston designed six-sided (hexagonal) bases for his Dickens characters, locking them mechanically to the Cottage background display. In 1946 he applied for a patent to protect this design motif and he cast the term "Patent Pending" into the base of each Dickens figurine.

In 1953 he was informed that the patent was denied. All Dickens production from 1946 to 1953 bears the term "Patent Pending."

SML 49 David Copperfield and Wife (*Pat. Pend.*)	49 SR 1946-1953
SML 49-A Copperfield and Wife	49-A SR 1953-1968
SML 49-B David and Dora Copperfield	49-B SR 1968-1975
	LR 1976-Present
	(No. 6102)

Prescott Baston began his Dickens series with David Copperfield and his first wife, Dora. Written in 1849 and 1850, *David Copperfield* emerged as Dickens' masterpiece. David's marriage to Dora Spenlow, a rattlebrained childlike woman is followed soon after by her death. David marries Agnes Wickfield at the end of the novel.

For no apparent reasons, Baston changed the title of the figurine from David to simply Copperfield when he removed the "Patent Pending" from the mold in 1953. Then, again for no reason, he added Dora's first name in 1968.

SML 50 Mr. Micawber (*Pat. Pend.*)	1946 SO SR 1946-1953
SML 50-A (*w/o Pat. Pend.*)	50-A SR 1954-1975
	LR 1976-Present
	(No. 6101)

Mr. Wilkins Micawber is a great projector of bubble schemes sure to lead to fortune but always ending in grief. In spite of his lack of results, he never despairs. He feels certain that something will "turn up." Having failed in every adventure in England, he emigrates to Australia where he becomes a magistrate. Micawber is said to be drawn from Dickens' father.

Baston drew his design from the epic portrayal of Micawber

by W. C. Fields in the 1936 MGM movie of *David Copperfield*. Baston sent Fields a Micawber figurine before it was introduced and received a note of approval in return. It was the same year the famous actor died.

SML 51 Aunt Betsy Trotwood (*Pat. Pend.*) 1946 51 SR 1946–1953
SML 51-A (*w/o Pat. Pend.*) 51-A SR 1954–1975
LR 1976–Present
(No. 6103)

Miss Betsy Trotwood is David Copperfield's great-aunt. She lives with Mr. Dick, the likeable lunatic. Miss Betsy's snappishness and briskness conceal a great tenderness of heart. She takes in the runaway Copperfield, defends him against Mr. Murdstone, and becomes devoted to him.

Baston portrays her carrying her umbrella and rushing off to the front yard to scare off the tourists riding on donkeys.

SML 52 Peggotty (*Pat. Pend.*) 1946 52 SR 1946–1953
SML 52-A (*w/o Pat. Pend.*) 1946 52-A SR 1954–1975
LR 1976–Present
(No. 6104)

Clara Peggotty is David's faithful nurse. With the other members of the Peggotty family (Dan'el, Em'ly and Ham), she is a great aid and comfort to him in his early childhood.

Baston portrays Peggotty seated on a trunk digging refreshments out of a picnic basket and "popping buttons off the back of her dress as she always did when she got excited."

SML 53 Barkis (*Pat. Pend.*) 1946 53 SR 1946–1953
SML 53-A (*w/o Pat. Pend.*) 53-A SR 1954–1975
LR 1976–Present
(No. 6105)

Barkis is a carrier who, in his gruff shyness, courts Peggotty by asking David to tell her that "Barkis is willin'." Peggotty takes the hint and becomes Mrs. Barkis.

Baston shows him "wearing a coat with a collar so high it pushes his hat forward, sleeves so long his hands disappear, and red glass buttons."

SML 54 Scrooge (*Pat. Pend.*) 1946 54 SR 1946–1953
SML 54-A (*w/o Pat. Pend.*) 54-A SR 1954–1975
LR 1976–Present
(No. 6112)

In Dickens' 1843 Christmas story, *A Christmas Carol*, the subject is the conversion of Ebenezer Scrooge, "a grasping old sinner," by a series of visions of Christmas past, present and to come. Scrooge has glimpses of his life as a schoolboy, apprentice and young lover; of the joyous home of Bob Cratchit, his underpaid clerk; of what his lot would be if he were to die now, heartless and despised. These visions wholly change his nature, and he becomes cheerful and benevolent. He loves all and is by all beloved. Although Dickens admits he started the story for the income it would bring, he said afterwards that he laughed and cried over it as he did over no other story.

Baston portrays the "before visions" miser holding an account book and calculating what some victim owes him.

SML 55 Bob Cratchit and Tiny Tim   1946 55 SR 1946–1953
    (*Pat. Pend.*)
SML 55-A (*w/o Pat. Pend.*)   55-A SR 1954–1975
                                         LR 1976–Present
                                           (No. 6111)

Bob Cratchit is Scrooge's underpaid clerk. Though Cratchit has to maintain nine dependents with his meager wages, his home, unlike his employer's, is filled with happiness and love. Tiny Tim, his little lame son, is a winsome and beloved child. In the ordinary course of events, he is doomed to an early death. But Scrooge, after his change of character, makes Tiny Tim his special charge.

Baston portrays the pair returning from church, Tim seated on his father's shoulder and Bob Cratchit decorated with "six foot of scarf exclusive of fringe."

SML 57 Songs at Cratchits (*Pat. Pend.*)   1946 57 SR 1946–1953
SML 57-A (*w/o Pat. Pend.*)   57-A SR 1954–1975
                                         LR 1976–Present
                                         (No. 6113)

As with Mrs. Cratchit, the Cratchit children serve as a loving background to the lives of Bob Cratchit and Tiny Tim in stark contrast to the penny-pinching and barren world of Ebenezer Scrooge.

SML 56 Mrs. Cratchit (*Pat. Pend.*)   1946 56 1946–1953
SML 56-A (*w/o Pat. Pend.*)   56-A SR 1954–1975
                                         LR 1976–Present
                                         (No. 6114)

Bob Cratchit's wife is a minor character in Dickens' story, serving primarily as a courageous and loving contrast to the world of Ebenezer Scrooge.

Baston portrays her "wearing a twice-turned gown made brave with a six pence worth of ribbon" and bringing a tiny plum pudding to the Cratchit's table.

SML 58 Mr. Pickwick (*Pat. Pend.*)   1946 58 SR 1946–1953
SML 58-A (*w/o Pat. Pend.*)   58-A SR 1954–1975
                                         LR 1976–Present
                                         (No. 6106)

Charles Dickens wrote the *Pickwick Papers* serially from 1836 to 1837 and it is made up of letters and manuscripts on the activities of the Pickwick Club. The chief character is Samuel Pickwick, founder of the Club, a most naive and benevolent elderly gentleman. As Chairman he travels about with his fellow club members and acts as their guardian and advisor.

Baston portrays Mr. Pickwick making notes "on his theory of tittlebats."

SML 59 Sam Weller (*Pat. Pend.*) 1946 59 SR 1946–1953
SML 59-A (*w/o Pat. Pend.*) 59-A SR 1954–1975
LR 1976–Present
(No. 6107)

Sam Weller is the center of comic interest in the *Pickwick Papers*. He is bootblack at the White Hart and afterward servant to Mr. Pickwick, to whom he becomes devotedly attached. When Pickwick is sent to the Fleet Prison, Weller, rather than leave his master, gets his father to arrest him for debt. "Bless his old gaiters," Weller cries out about Pickwick, "I never seen such a fine creature in my days. Blessed if I don't think his heart must ha'been born 25 year arter his body, at least."

Baston portrays him polishing boots while seated on a pile of hay. Weller is saying, "Ask him if he wants them now, or will he wait until he gets them."

SML 61 Dickens' Cottage (*Pat. Pend.*) 1946 61 SR 1946–1953
SML 61-A (*w/o Pat. Pend.*) 61-A SR 1954–1975
LR 1976–Present
(No. 6116)

Baston concluded his 1946 design of twelve Dickens characters with a backdrop for the collection. Purely fanciful in detail, the base is edged with the mechanical slots into which the various figures are positioned. Three more figurines (1948 and 1949) and a collection base (1966) were yet to be designed.

SML 60 Sairey Gamp and Mrs. Harris 1946 60 SR 1946–1953
(*Pat. Pend.*)
SML 60-A (*w/o Pat. Pend.*) 60-A SR 1954–1975
LR 1976–Present
(No. 6108)

Sarah Gamp (better known as Sairey) is a major character in Dickens' *Martin Chuzzlewit* and is one of the best known of all his characters. She is a totally disreputable nurse, famous for her bulky umbrella and perpetual reference to Mrs. Harris, a purely imaginary person whose opinions, always quoted by Sairey, always confirm Sairey's opinions. Hence, a "regular Gamp" came to signify a low-class, drink-sodden, uncertificated maternity nurse. An umbrella, particularly a large, badly rolled cotton one, came to be called a gamp.

Over the years, many collectors have been confused by the six-sided disc with the words "Mrs. Harris" inscribed on the surface. She's not there because she never was.

SML 62 Puritan Spinner 1946 C 1946 300

In the midst of his 1946 retail design work, Baston was approached by the president of the Puritan Candy Co. in neighboring Somerville, Massachusetts. The company wanted a small figurine of a Puritan woman at her spinning wheel, the company's trademark. Baston produced 300 pieces, painted with a blue dress, and never received another order. However, as with the first Shaker Glen House request eight years earlier, the Puritan Spinner showed him an entirely different market for his work than the retail business through Carbone. The Puritan Spinner is truly the forerunner of the Jell-O series, the Shawmut Indian, *Reader's Digest* and *Saturday Evening Post* series.

The Puritan Candy Co. no longer exists.

SML 64 Down East   1947 64 SR 1947–1948
SML 64-A A Farmer's Wife   64-A SR 1949–1975
                                           LR 1977–Present
                                              (No. 6227)

Farmer's Wife was designed as a pair with Farmer. Originally titled "Down East" from the John Gould story "The Farmer Takes a Wife," Baston changed the title to Farmer's Wife in 1949.

She is sitting on the back steps peeling apples and tossing the peelings to a couple of hens.

SML 63 Satchel-Eye Dyer   1946 63 SR 1946–1948
SML 63-A Farmer   63-A SR 1949–1975
                                           LR 1977–Present
                                              (No. 6226)

SML 63-B Farmer Penstand   63-B SR 1958–1967

Baston designed a pair for his new distributor, Schmid Bros., in the end of 1946 and beginning of 1947. He took two characters from John Gould's Down-East story "The Farmer Takes a Wife," Satchel-Eye Dyer and his wife. No one knew who Satchel-Eye Dyer was, so Baston changed the title to "Farmer" two years later.

The figurine was converted into a penstand and was sold through retail stores from 1958 to 1967.

SML 65 Lobsterman   1947 SR 1947–1975
                                           LR 1976–Present
                                              (No. 6201)

Baston designed Lobsterman, and Sampling the Stew as a Maine couple, along with Farmer and Farmer's Wife.

Until the mid-1940's, before the lobster market was developed as a gourmet delight, New England lobsters were "the poor man's food." A proud New Englander would hide the lobster shells in the garbage so neighbors wouldn't know they couldn't afford better.

SML 66 First Cookbook Author	1947 66 SR 1947–1948
SML 66-A Sampling the Stew	66-A SR 1948–1975
	LR 1976–Present
	(No. 6202)
SML 66-B Sampling the Stew Penstand	66-B SR 1958–1967
SML 66-C Yankee Kitchen	66-C SR 1948–1950

Baston designed Sampling the Stew to accompany the Lobsterman.

First named "First Cookbook Author," the title was changed to Sampling the Stew one year after introduction. The design was incorporated into a penstand from 1958 to 1967.

Baston's new distributor, Schmid Bros., employed a Texas salesman who insisted the design would sell in the South if it was titled "Yankee Kitchen." Baston created a new mold, the new title did not help sales in Texas, and production of Yankee Kitchen was stopped in 1950.

SML 67 Trout Fisherman	1947 66 SR 1947–1948
SML 67-A Down Stream	67-A SR 1948–1975
	LR 1979–Present
	(No. 6506)
SML 68 Fisherman's Wife	1947 68 SR 1947–1975
SML 69 Fisher Pair Penstand	69 SR 1958–1967

Baston designed this pair for Schmid as part of his early husband and wife pairs. The Fisherman was titled "Trout Fisherman" and then in 1948 took on its current title.

The figurines were sold as a set until they were incorporated into one penstand in 1958. The designs were never popular sellers and are relatively rare Sebastian retail miniatures.

SML 70 Amish Man   1947 70 SR 1947–1975
                                        LR 1977–Present
                                        (No. 6224)

SML 71 Amish Folk   71 SR 1947–1975
                                        LR 1977–Present
                                        (No. 6225)

Baston had just begun work with Schmid Bros. and the first appearance of the line was scheduled for a department store in York, Pennsylvania, center of the Pennsylvania Dutch country. He designed these pieces specifically for that appearance and they have remained in the line since then.

The Amish are one of the most conservative sects of the Mennonite Church. Noted for their independence, the Amish preserve simplicity of dress and habits.

SML 72 The Pilgrims   1947 72 SR 1947–1957
SML 72-A Thanksgiving Couple   72-A SR 1958–1967
SML 72-B Pilgrim Couple   72-B SR 1968–1975
                                        LR 1976–Present
                                        (No. 6324)

Originally designed on speculation for the Toll House restaurant in Whitman, Massachusetts, the Pilgrims were sold at retail through Schmid Bros. from the beginning. The base was changed to a more ornate base in 1958 (on a speculative promotion with a bank to provide interchangeable couples in a bank-provided recessed penstand), and the name was changed to

Thanksgiving Couple. In 1968 the title was once again changed to its present title, Pilgrim Couple.

The Pilgrim is portrayed carrying a turkey while his wife carries a basket of assorted vegetables.

SML 73 Henry VIII   1947 SR 1947–1975
SML 74 Anne Boleyn

Baston began the design of his Shakespearean series with three pairs in 1947. Henry and Anne are portrayed from The Famous History of the Life of Henry VIII (1613). Henry, who has met Anne, becomes concerned with the legal aspects of his marriage to Katherine of Aragon. Through Wolsey, he negotiates with the Pope for a divorce. But when Wolsey discovers that the King plans to marry Anne, he tries to stop the divorce, is found out, and, while under arrest for treason, dies. Henry's marriage is annulled by the Archbishop of Canterbury and he marries Anne.

SML 75 Falstaff   1947 SR 1947–1975
SML 76 Mistress Ford

In The Merry Wives of Windsor (1598), Sir John Falstaff, knowing that Mistress Ford controls the purse strings in her household, decides to seduce her. She learns of his scheme and decides to make a fool of him. Mr. Ford, who doubts his wife's fidelity, pretends to be another aspirant for Mistress Ford's favors and engages Falstaff to intercede for him. After several misadventures, the old lecher learns of their plot. They pardon him.

SML 77 Romeo   **1947 SR 1947–1975**
SML 78 Juliet

Shakespeare's *Romeo and Juliet* (1596) has been popularized on stage, screen, radio, television and opera. Romeo Montague and Juliet Capulet suffer their love and marriage in the midst of the deadly feud of their families. At the end, he poisons himself and she stabs herself at his body. Realizing their hatred has caused the tragedy, the two houses make a tardy, sorrowful peace.

Baston mounted the couple on a common base in 1958 (SML 289).

SML 81 Dahl's Fisherman   **1947 SR 1947–1975**

Dahl's portrayal is of a crusty pipe-smoking Yankee fisherman stepping from his boat and lugging a large codfish. The figurine was sold by Stearns and other Boston gift stores.

SML 79 Mr. Beacon Hill   **1947 SR 1947–1975**
SML 80 Mrs. Beacon Hill

In 1947, the R. H. Stearns Co., the most lavish department store in Boston at that time, celebrated the 100th anniversary of its founding in 1847. They commissioned John Dahl, the *Boston Herald* cartoonist, to caricature "typical" Bostonians. Dahl had portrayed "Mr. and Mrs. Salton-Cabot," and Stearns renamed them "Mr. and Mrs. Beacon Hill."

He is proceeding across the Boston Common with his umbrella and green baize bag "which proper Bostonians of Harvard extraction carry." He is surrounded by squirrels and pigeons.

She is shown waiting "under the clock at R. H. Stearns." Her husband will take her to the Waldorf cafeteria on Tremont Street. She carries the inevitable umbrella. The figurines were distributed both by Stearns and by Schmid Bros. to Boston gift stores.

The Stearns store at 140 Tremont Street and later at Chestnut Hill shopping center closed in the early 1970's.

SML 82 Dilemma—The Boston Common Cow (*Purple*)
                                    1947 80 SR 1947–1948
SML 82-A (*Brown Cow*)   **80-A SR 1949–1975**

Cleveland Amory, in his *Proper Bostonian*, points out an old Boston law still on the books. If you have a house on the Boston Common and a person presents himself with a cow, you are legally, if not morally, required to allow him to lead the cow through your house. Dahl picked up on this with Dilemma, the cow with no cowpaths. Dahl further portrayed the cow in front of the Massachusetts State House, "hanging around because there's so much bull inside."

Baston first painted him purple ("I've never seen a purple cow," etc.) but changed him to the more popular brown. The figurine was sold by Stearns and Boston gift stores.

SML 83 Outboard Motor Couple   1947 SR 1947–1975
LR 1979–Present
(No. 6507)

Baston designed a figurine for Travelers Insurance Co. in Hartford, Connecticut, that illustrated a couple enjoying the benefits of retirement. Travelers did not go ahead with the program and Baston immediately switched production to his gift shops.

SML 84 George Washington   1947 SR 1947–1975
LR 1976–Oct. 31, 1980
(Discontinued Forever)

From 1946 to 1953, Prescott Baston petitioned the Guggenheim Foundation for a grant to design all the presidents of the United States for use in educating school children. The grant was never awarded him.

In 1947, Baston designed Washington, Lincoln and FDR to demonstrate his plan. All three designs were issued in 1947 through Carbone.

The George Washington design was continued by Lance in 1976 and then was discontinued forever in 1980.

SML 85 Abraham Lincoln (*Looking Ahead*) 1947 85 SR 1947–1958
SML 85-A Abraham Lincoln (*Looking Down*)   85-A SR 1958–1975
LR 1976–Present
(Discontinued Oct. 31, 1982)
SML 85-B Penstand   85-B SR 1958–1967

Baston designed Abraham Lincoln in 1947. In 1958, after he had designed his Lincoln Memorial (SML 291), he replaced the head looking straight ahead with the new design, looking down. He also increased the base size.

A paperweight/penstand was provided on special order during the years 1958 to 1967.

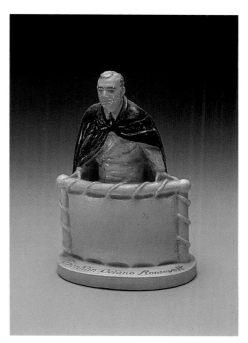

SML 86 Franklin Delano Roosevelt   1947 SR 1947–1975

Franklin Delano Roosevelt as president spanned Prescott Baston's life from age 23 to 36, an incredible 13 years. Roosevelt took office during the bottom of the nation's Depression and presided over the country's participation in New Deal welfare legislation and Lend-lease mobilization. He emerged in 1945 as the most powerful leader in the world.

Baston portrayed FDR in the early Thirties, before the pressures had taken their toll. The pose, standing at a railroad car railing, followed the silently-agreed-upon policy of never showing him as crippled.

SML 87 Princess Elizabeth   1947 SR 1947
SML 88 Prince Philip

Princess Elizabeth and Prince Philip were married Nov. 20, 1947, at Westminster Abbey. As with the marriage of her son, Prince Charles, in 1981, a large assortment of commemorative objects were developed.

Baston designed the pair following the announcement of their engagement in early 1947 and proceeded with sales as soon as the wedding date was announced. He sold approximately 2,000 sets through the Boston area and then demand ended abruptly.

SML 89 R. H. Stearns 1847 Couple	1947 89 C 1947–8 8,500
SML 89-A Godey Couple	89-A SR 1948–1957
SML 89-B Victorian Couple	89-B SR 1958–1975
	LR 1976–Present
	(No. 6325)

The R. H. Stearns Co. store in downtown Boston celebrated its 100th anniversary in 1947. Mr. Schultze, president of the company, ordered 500 figurines depicting an 1840's couple shopping together. The design, with 1847 cast in the base, was sold for $1.00 through store sales, contests and an elaborate Christmas mail program. Altogether, Baston produced 8,500 figurines in 1947 and 1948.

In 1948 he removed the "1847" and sold the design as the "Godey Couple," dressed in costumes illustrated in *Godey's Ladies Book*. In 1958 he placed the couple on an ornate base for inclusion with other couples as "Victorian Couple."

SML 90 In the Candy Store (*Necco*)	1947 90 C 1947 5,000
SML 90-A In the Candy Store	90-A SR 1949–1975
	LR 1976–Present
	(No. 6221)
SML 90-B In the Candy Store Penstand	90-B C 1959 1,000

The Necco Candy Co. in Cambridge celebrated its 100th anniversary in 1947, the same year as the Stearns' centennial. An engineer who worked with Baston at Greer's during the war returned to his job at Necco. He told Baston of the company's plans, Baston contacted the company and they agreed on a design. The first and only order for the figurine was for 5,000 pieces. The "Necco" on the right side of the candy counter is in bright red.

In 1949, Baston received permission to remove the "Necco" emphasis and place the design through retail distribution. It has remained one of the most popular Sebastians to this day.

In 1958, when he was converting some designs to penstands, he received an additional 1,000 piece order from Necco for the 11-year-old design.

| SML 92 Toll House Town Crier | 1947 92 C 1947–1949 4,000 |
| SML 92-A Toll House Town Crier Penstand | 92-A C 1959 500 |

Baston knew the Wakefields, the people who owned the Toll House Restaurant in Whitman, Massachusetts. They asked him to design a figurine for use in a national advertising program promoting their Toll House chocolate chip cookies. He produced 4,000 pieces for them over a three-year period. In 1959, when the penstands were being promoted, the company purchased 500 designs mounted on a larger base.

In 1950, Baston changed the cap from tri-corner to Puritan, added a cape, and sold the design through his gift shops as the "Town Crier" (SML 151).

SML 91 Howard Johnson Pieman   1947 C 300

Howard Johnson's restaurant in Quincy, Massachusetts was a small cafe that had survived the Depression and was beginning to flex its muscles with plans for national distribution. Although the restaurant did not have a gift shop at that time (!), they contacted Baston to design and produce 300 figurines that they used for publicity purposes.

SML 93 Shawmut Indian (*Painted*)   1947 93 C 1947–1961 25,000
SML 93-A (*Modified, smaller*)   93-A C 1962–Present 65,000

A Professor Ames of Harvard, doing research on "typical Indian heads," sculpted an Indian bust that the Shawmut Bank in Boston adopted as their trademark. From 1947 on, Baston produced 90,000 of these miniatures, making the design the most widely available of all Sebastians. The bank used them as investment incentives and advertising premiums. Production was continued right up through Lance production and in some years production went as high as 5,000 pieces in a run.

Three designs were used, the original painted and a modified sculpture with gold and bronze paint. The modification took place in 1961. Baston and a woman painter did the bulk of the featuring on the painted version.

SML 95 Huckleberry Finn   1948 SR 1948–1975
                                         LR 1976–Present
                                         (No. 6133)

Huck Finn is Tom Sawyer's parentless friend and stands in contrast to Tom's well-ordered, obedient life of respectable duty.

Baston portrays Huck sleepily fishing, "letting the fish do all the work."

SML 94 Tom Sawyer   1948 94 SR 1948–1975
                                      LR 1976–Present
                                      (No. 6132)
SML 94-A Tom Sawyer Penstand   94-A C 1958 200
         (*Carmote Paint*)

As with Dickens, Prescott Baston has read all of Mark Twain's work. But unlike some of the more obscure Dickens favorites (Pecksniff, Barkis, etc.) Baston went right to the six most popular characters in Twain's most popular novel, *Tom Sawyer* (1876).

Here, Tom is trying to figure out a way to avoid the fence painting. His cat, after the medicine, is duly apprehensive.

In 1958, Baston placed the design on a penstand base inscribed "Carmote Paint" and sold 200 to the Carpenter-Morton Paint Company for their promotional use.

SML 96 Becky Thatcher   1948 SR 1948–1975
                                         LR 1976–Present
                                         (No. 6131)

Becky Thatcher, daughter of the Judge, is Tom's girlfriend and is trapped with him in the cave where Injun Joe has hidden.

Baston portrays her standing at her schoolroom desk, holding behind her back a peach which Tom has passed to her. He has written on her slate "Please take it. I have more."

57

SML 97 Aunt Polly   1948 SR 1948–1975
                                          LR 1976–Present
                                          (No. 6135)

Tom Sawyer's Aunt Polly is the model of Midwest respectability. Tom and Huck's antics drive her to distraction at times, but her deep love for Tom is always apparent and available.

SML 99 Judge Thatcher   1948 SR 1948–1975
                                          LR 1976–Present
                                          (No. 6134)

Judge Thatcher is Becky's father and also presides over Muff Potter's trial where Tom reveals that Injun Joe is the killer.

SML 98 Jim   1948 SR 1948–1975
                                          LR 1976–Present
                                          (No. 6136)

Jim is the black friend of Huckleberry Finn. In the novel, *The Adventures of Huckleberry Finn*, Huck and Jim float the Mississippi River on a raft and philosophize on the state of man and his world.

SML 100 Slalom   1948 SR 1948–1950
SML 101 Sitzmark

Baston designed Slalom and Sitzmark for his gift shops. The problem was that ski fashions changed too rapidly. Baston would have had to change his molds every year and sales did not warrant the expense.

SML 104 Swedish Boy   1948 SR 1948–1954
SML 105 Swedish Girl

Baston designed Swedish Boy and Swedish Girl for the
Svenska Kaffe Stuga in Sudbury, Massachusetts. That same
year and for the next several years, the pair was sold in Worcester, Massachusetts gift shops and one shop in Delaware. It was
always a Scandinavian specialty item and was discontinued in
1954. Approximately 500 sets were sold in all.

Baston used formal dress as illustrated in a book on the
Dalarna province of Sweden and "Sverige Dalarna" is cast into
the base.

SML 102 Mr. Rittenhouse Square   1948 102 SR 1948–1951
SML 103 Mrs. Rittenhouse Square   103 SR 1948–1951
SML 103-A (*Scheie Eye Institute*)   103-A C 1981

A Philadelphia store owner saw Mr. & Mrs. Beacon Hill (SML
79–80) and wanted a pair "just as stuffy" for Philadelphia. Mr.
Rittenhouse Square wears a homburg and formal morning
dress and illustrates his background beside containers filled
with Scrapple. Mrs. is museum-hopping and disdainfully gaz-
ing through her lorgnette at a bust of Benjamin Franklin. The
store never sold many and the pair was discontinued after a few
years.

Mrs. Rittenhouse Square was reintroduced to retail sales in
1981 to raise funds for Philadelphia's Scheie Eye Institute. The
words "Scheie Eye Institute" are permanently cast into the base
of the recent issue.

SML 106 Little Nell and Her Grandfather 1948 106 SR 1948–1953
     (*Pat. Pend.*)
SML 106-A (*w/o Pat. Pend.*)   106-A SR 1954–1975
                       LR 1976–Present
                       (No. 6110)

Dickens wrote *The Old Curiosity Shop* in 1840. The heroine,
Nell Trent, lives with her grandfather who owns a curiosity
shop. The grandfather, an obsessive gambler, loses all he has
and he and Little Nell are forced to leave the shop and roam
about the countryside as beggars. Written in serial install-
ments, Americans would wait every month to hear the latest
exploits of Little Nell.

SML 107 Pecksniff (*Pat. Pend.*)   **1948 107 SR 1948–1953**
SML 107-A (*w/o Pat. Pend.*)   **107-A SR 1954–1975**
                                LR 1976–Present
                                (No. 6109)

In Dickens' *Martin Chuzzlewit* (1844), Seth Pecksniff is drawn as a vain hypocrite who is eventually exposed and denounced by Chuzzlewit, Sr., for trying to force Mary Graham to marry him. Baston portrays him as a pompous ass standing beside the bust he has made of himself.

had not needed the GOP design since Truman walked away with the election. A total of 800 sets were sold and then were discontinued.

SML 108 Democratic Victory   **1948 SR 1948**
SML 109 Republican Victory

The year 1948 was an election year. As everyone knew, Dewey would trounce President Truman, but just to hedge his bet, Baston also designed a Democratic Victory. As it turned out, he

SML 110 Nathaniel Hawthorne   **1948 SR 1948–1975**

Nathaniel Hawthorne (1804–1864), American author with his roots deeply embedded in New England, was the beginning of another Baston literary series, The House of Seven Gables. Hawthorne is portrayed here at his desk in the Boston Customs House where he worked during the period before his writing career had begun. Baston depicts the three-legged stool he described in one of his novels and shows Hawthorne holding a replica of his account book which is on exhibit at the Customs House.

SML 111 House of Seven Gables	1948 111 SR 1948–1975
	LR 1976–Present
	(No. 6121)
SML 111-A (*Salem Rotary Club*)	111-A C 1953–1975 700
SML 111-B (*Tape Measure*)	111-B C 1956 200

The House of Seven Gables is both an historic Colonial house in Salem, Mass., and the backdrop for Nathaniel Hawthorne's novel (1851). Salem is a seaport adjacent to Baston's Marblehead and plays an important part in New England history.

Baston is a member of the Marblehead Rotary Club and attends makeup meetings in Salem. He designed a Salem Rotary symbol on the base and supplied them with 700 pieces over the years for fund-raising, gifts to visitors, etc.

In 1956, a Salem hardware store ordered 200 Houses with retractable measuring tapes built into them.

SML 112 Spirit of '76	1948 112 SR 1948–1975
	LR 1976–Present
	(No. 6213)
SML 112-A (*Penstand Painted*)	112-A SR 1958–1967
SML 112-B (*Penstand Bronzed*)	112-B SR 1958–1967
SML 112-C (*Marblehead Savings Bank*) Penstand	
	112-C C 1959 1,000

Archibald Willard was an unknown wagon painter in Ohio when he was commissioned in 1876 to sketch a scene for the approaching Centennial Exposition in Philadelphia. The result was perhaps America's most famous patriotic painting. Willard's painting now hangs in the Selectman's Room of Abbot Hall in Marblehead, a few hundred yards from Baston's studio.

In 1958, Baston began producing painted and bronzed penstands and, in 1959, produced 1,000 penstands for the Marblehead Savings Bank.

SML 113 Jordan Marsh Observer   1948 C 1948–1953 5,000

The Jordan Marsh Co. in Boston had a figure in colonial dress painted on a billboard overlooking the construction site for their new store. The store advertising department had Baston design and produce a figurine depicting the character. The design was popular, Baston produced several hundred at a time until 1953, and the Observer became a trademark long after the construction was completed and the sidewalk superintendents had returned home.

In 1958, the figure, with lobster trap and ship's wheel, was used for two more promotions (SML 298). These designs were finally converted to Colonial Overseer in 1972.

SML 115 A Harvey Girl   1948 C 1948–1949 1,500

Harvey restaurants dotted the Great West, tracing the growth and prosperity of the Atchison, Topeka and Santa Fe railroad. The restaurants became an institution with Western travelers as did the distinctive costumes of the waitresses, the Harvey Girls.

A Carbone gift salesman, traveling from Chicago to Los Angeles, got the idea for this promotion and sold it to restaurant management in Los Angeles. The first order was for 1,000 pieces and the reorder, a year later, for 500. The figurine was used for railroad advertising.

SML 114 Mr. Sheraton   1948 C 1948 200

The Sheraton Hotel chain is headquartered in Boston. In 1948 they asked Baston to design and produce 200 "Mr. Sheratons." Baston portrayed a gentleman in period dress standing in front of a Sheraton bookcase.

SML 116 Mary Lyon   1948 C 1948 750

Mary Lyon was the founder of Mount Holyoke College in South Hadley, Mass. School officials requested a Sebastian Miniature depicting Mary Lyon for their use in fund-raising activities.

Baston portrayed her lecturing before a group on the benefits of education for a young woman. She has a green cloth bag, with which she always carried home the money.

SML 117 Uncle Mistletoe 1949 C 1949 1,500
LR 1979 500

Uncle Mistletoe and Aunt Holly were once the very popular Christmas trademarks of Marshall Field and Company, the giant Chicago department store. The store advertising department had seen the R. H. Stearns Sebastian two years before, and commissioned Baston to create an Uncle Mistletoe figurine. He produced 1,500 for the store's Christmas season.

Marshall Field ordered 500 more in 1979, thirty years later. By then, Uncle Mistletoe was a thing of the past and few remembered the elfin character.

SML 118 Eustace Tilley 1949 C 1949 500

Eustace Tilley, Esq., is the trademark of *The New Yorker* magazine. He graces its front cover once every year. The magazine's Circulation Department commissioned Baston to create a Eustace Tilley figurine. He captured the haughty gentleman peering through his pince-nez at a nonexistent butterfly. The magazine used 500 that year for a promotion.

SML 119 Menotomy Indian (*Trust*)	1949 119 C 1949-1951 2,500
SML 119-A (*Bronzed Figurine*)	119-A SR 1952-1975
SML 119-B (*Painted Figurine*)	119-B SR 1952-1975
SML 119-C (*Bronzed Penstand*)	119-C SR 1958-1967
SML 119-D (*Dartmouth*)	119-D C 1955 50

The Menotomy Trust Company in Arlington, Mass., asked Baston to replicate in miniature the bronze sculpture of a Menotomy Indian originally sculpted by Cyrus Dallin. He produced a figurine with "Menotomy Trust" inscribed in the base and sold 2,500 in three years.

In 1952 he removed that inscription and issued the design both painted and bronzed to his gift shops. He issued a bronze penstand from 1958 to 1967 and, in 1955, he produced a special edition of 50 with "Dartmouth College" cast into the base.

SML 120 Boy Scout Plaque 1949 C 1949–1951 2,500

The Boy Scouts of America, headquartered in East Brunswick, New Jersey, asked Baston to design a "patriotic" Boy Scout figurine for sale in their stores and catalogs. If the Boy Scout kneeling with a United States Great Shield in front of the Statue of Liberty is not enough, he titled the plaque "Strengthen the Arm of Liberty."

Baston sold 2,500 during a three-year period and then offered it to his gift shops without success.

SML 121 John Hancock 1949 121 C 1949–1975 12,000
SML 121-A (Penstand) 121-A C 1959 3,000

Baston created a miniature in full color of the four-foot bronze sculpture in the lobby of the John Hancock Insurance Company. Given to the insurance company's best customers, this figurine represented a very steady business over a 25-year period.

In 1959, Baston created a special penstand used by the company in a national promotion to real estate developers.

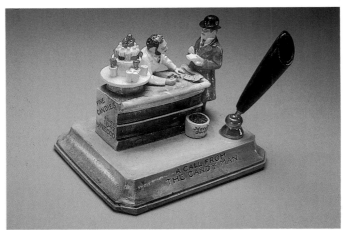

SML 122 A Call From the Candyman (*Necco*) Penstand
1949 122 C 1949–1950 1,000
SML 122-A A Corner Drug Store 122-A SR 1951–1975
LR 1976–Present
(No. 6211)

The Necco Candy Co. in Cambridge (see "In the Candy Store" SML 90) commissioned a large penstand order portraying an old-fashioned candy salesman calling on an old-fashioned drugstore owner.

The resulting design had the words "Fine Candies since 1847 by Necco" highlighted in red on the end of the counter and "A Call From the Candyman" cast into the base. Necco salesmen handed this out to their customers. This was Baston's first penstand design.

In 1951, Baston removed the large base and titled the figurine "Corner Drug Store."

SML 123 Santa Claus 1949 123 SR 1949–1975
LR 1976–Present
(No. 6222)

SML 123-A Cleveland Issue 123-A C 1955 400
SML 123-B 1980 Issue 123-B C 1980 1,000
SML 123-C 1981 Ornament 123-C SR 1981 5,000

The movie "Miracle on 34th Street" appeared during the 1947 Christmas season and, when it reappeared during the 1948 season it had become a classic. Macy's department store, featured in the film, asked Baston to design a Santa. The design has sold briskly since then.

In 1955, Halle's department store asked for a Santa without the lamp and replaced with the street intersection of Euclid and Huron. They bought 400 pieces. In 1980, Blair's commissioned

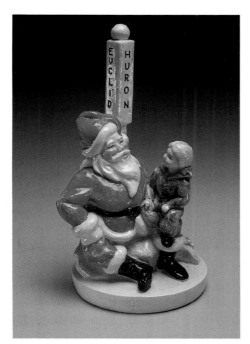

SML 125 Patrick Henry   1949 SR 1949–1975
SML 126 Sarah Henry

The Henrys are characteristic of Baston's Early Couples, but Patrick Henry (1736–1799) posed next to a free-standing podium. The pair was issued on the 150th anniversary of his death.

As a member of the Virginia House of Burgesses, he offered a series of resolutions against the Stamp Act. He later served in the Continental Congress and as governor of Virginia. His most famous speech:

"Is life so dear, or peace so sweet, as to be purchased at the price of chains and slavery? Forbid it, Almighty God! I know not what course others may take; but as for me, give me liberty or give me death!"

a Santa with the year "1980" lettered on the lamp and then sealed. Finally, in 1981, Gift Creations, a retail purchasing and cataloging center in St. Paul, Minnesota, asked for a Santa with a wire hook cast in the pole to serve as a Christmas tree ornament hanger.

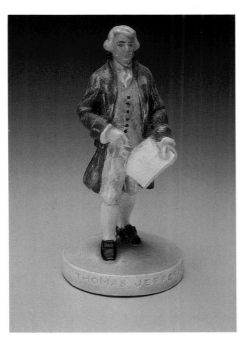

SML 124 Thomas Jefferson   1949 SR 1949–1975
                                   LR 1975-Present
                                     (No. 6003)

Thomas Jefferson (1743–1826), author of the Declaration of Independence, founder of the University of Virginia, overseer of the Louisiana Purchase and third President of the United States, joined Baston's gallery of presidents in 1949. Baston's characterization is inspired by the Rudolph Evans statue of Jefferson in the Jefferson Memorial in Washington, D.C., dedicated six years earlier.

SML 127 Oliver Twist and The Parish Beadle
    (*Pat. Pend.*)   1949 127 SR 1949–1953
SML 127-A (*w/o Pat. Pend.*)   127-A SR 1954–1975
                                     LR 1976–Present
                                     (No. 6115)

Baston designed Oliver Twist as the final character in the Dickens series except for Dickens himself in 1952 and a base to house the collection in 1966.

The novel *Oliver Twist* (1837–1839) depicts the world of poverty, crime and the workhouses of 19th century London. Baston depicts young Oliver clutching the cuff of the parish beadle (an inferior church officer having a variety of minor duties). He is being led from the orphanage to his job as apprentice to an undertaker. He has all his worldly possessions in "a box six inches square and four inches deep."

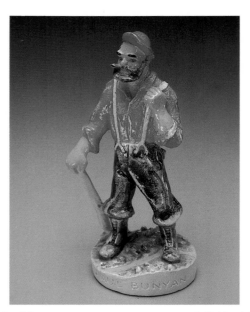

SML 128 Paul Bunyan   1949 SR 1949–1975
LR 1976–Oct. 31, 1978
(Discontinued Forever)

The legend of Paul Bunyan may have first appeared in Quebec or Northern Ontario. James Stevens traced him to a French Canadian logger named Paul Bunyan, who won a reputation as a fighter in the Papineau Rebellion against England in 1837. His popularity remains undiminished in the American northwest forests.

Baston designed the lumberman straddling a small river where houses can be seen between his feet. In July, 1978, the company announced the figurine would be the second to be discontinued forever at the end of October (see Lexington Minuteman; SML 361). Subsequent publicity in the limited edition collectibles marketplace has established Paul Bunyan as one of the most popular and sought-after Sebastian Miniatures.

SML 129 Betsy Ross   1949 SR 1949–1975
LR 1976–Present
(No. 6004)

Elizabeth Griscom Ross (1752–1836), Philadelphia, is known to have sewed American flags during the Revolution. The long-accepted story that she designed and made the first American national flag (The Stars and Stripes) is now generally discredited.

Baston's design was at the explicit request of the Betsy Ross House in Philadelphia. The Chippendale chair is a miniature replica of the chair in the house.

SML 130 Emmett Kelly   1949 130 C 1949–1951 1,000
SML 130-A The Clown   130-A SR 1952–1975
LR 1976–Oct. 31, 1979
(Discontinued Forever)

Prescott, Marjorie and Woody, age four, traveled the Fall of 1949 to Sarasota, Florida, the winter home of the Ringling Bros., Barnum and Bailey circus. The circus performed only under tent those years, so the South was a winter refuge. At the request of John Ringling North and Henry North, the circus owners, he designed an Emmett Kelly figurine displaying the famous clown during his tramp routine. The circus used 1,000 figurines, sending them to newspapers in towns where they were going to appear.

Converted to the retail "Clown" in 1952, The Clown was discontinued forever on October 31, 1979.

SML 131 Giant Royal Bengal Tiger   1949 C 1949–1951 300
                                             SR 1952–1975

Baston sculpted the Ringling Bros. tiger at the same time as Emmett Kelly (see SML 130). Approximately 300 of the tiger were used by the circus for the same publicity purposes as the Kelly figurine.

Baston offered the figurine through his retail dealers when Ringling Bros. completed their campaign.

SML 132 Yankee Sea Captain   1949 SR 1949–1975
                                       LR 1976–Present
                                       (No. 6241)

In 1949, Baston began design of historical sea figures. Following research at the Peabody Museum in Salem, he designed Yankee Sea Captain (1949), Donald McKay and Tom Bowline (1950).

The young captain is standing at the gangway of his Clipper ship. He is supervising the stowing of cargo before his departure to China. He holds the captain's horn.

SML 133 The Thinker (*Bronzed*)   1949 133 SR 1949–1975
SML 133-A Thinker Penstand   133-A SR 1958–1967

Baston sculpted a replica of Auguste Rodin's (1840–1917) Thinker (*Le Penseur*) for the gift shop in New York City's Metropolitan Museum of Art. He also distributed the bronzed figurine through his gift stores and, from 1958–1967, also provided a silvered design as a penstand.

Baston sold the piece regularly through the years and experienced a "minor boom" every Spring when the figurine was purchased as a graduation gift.

SML 134 The Mark Twain Home 　　　1949 C 1949–1950 300
in Hannibal, Missouri

Baston designed a replica of Mark Twain's home for a gift shop in Hannibal, Missouri. He designed the home emphasizing the fence where Tom Sawyer manipulated his chums into white-washing the fence. The gift shop sold some 300 pieces over a two-year period.

SML 137 Mary Had a Little Lamb 　　　1949 SR 1949–1975
LR 1976–Present
(No. 6403)

In 1949, Prescott Baston designed three nursery rhymes for "in the round." They were planned to be placed on music boxes where they would rotate while a tune would play. The plan never worked with the music box supplier and Baston sold them as popular figurines for over 30 years.

"Mary Had a Little Lamb" portrays the original "Little Red School House" in Sudbury, Massachusetts where Mary and her lamb meet her teacher.

SML 135 Dutchman's Pipe 　　　　　　1949 SR 1949
SML 136 Gathering Tulips

Schmid Bros. salesmen were attempting to place Sebastian Miniatures nationally. One of their salesmen persuaded Baston to design a Dutch pair for a gift shop in Holland, Michigan, site of the annual Tulip Festival. Only 100 sets were produced. This is a very rare Sebastian set.

SML 138 The Cow Jumped Over The Moon 　　1949 SR 1949–1975
LR 1976–Present
(No. 6402)

In this remarkable child's figurine we see a cat and a fiddle and a cow unsuccessfully attempting a jump over the moon. The little dog is laughing to see such sport and the dish is running away with the spoon.

SML 139 Jack and Jill   1949 SR 1949–1975
                                          LR 1976–Present
                                          (No. 6401)

As the music box rotates, Jack and Jill go up the hill and then tumble down. In this tiny scene, the crown of Jack's hat is broken.

SML 141 Katrina Van Tassel   1949 141 SR 1949–1975
SML 141-A (*Society member*)
                          141-A LR March 1, 1982 to Aug. 30, 1983

Katrina Van Tassel is the young lady courted by Ichabod Crane in Irving's *The Legend of Sleepy Hollow*. Here she responds to Crane's dance instructions, infuriating Brom Bones, Crane's rival.

The Society reissued Katrina as a member-only figurine from March, 1982 to August, 1983.

SML 140 Ichabod Crane   1949 140 SR 1949–1975
SML 140-A (*Society member*)   140-A LR Sept. 1, 1981 to
                                             Aug. 30, 1983

Washington Irving (1783–1859) wrote *The Legend of Sleepy Hollow* as a short story in his *Sketch Book of Geoffrey Crayon, Gent.* The story takes place at Sleepy Hollow, now Tarrytown, New York. Ichabod Crane, the local schoolmaster, courts Katrina Van Tassel, the town beauty. In this depiction, he demonstrates an intricate step to Miss Van Tassel.

In 1981, the Sebastian Collectors Society reissued the design, available only to members and planned for permanent retirement August 30, 1983.

SML 142 Brom Bones   1949 SR 1949–1975
          (*The Headless Horseman*)

Brom Bones, Ichabod Crane's rival for the affection of Katrina Van Tassel, puts a blanket over his head, tucks a pumpkin under his arm, and rides past Crane one dark night. Pretending to be a legendary decapitated Hessian horseman, he throws the pumpkin at the dismayed Ichabod and frightens the schoolmaster out of town.

The horse in this figurine is later to appear under Paul Revere (SML 152) and the Jordan Marsh Observer (SML 190). The Society will reissue Brom Bones for members-only from September, 1982 to August, 1983.

SML 145 Diedrich Knickerbocker   1950 SR 1950–1975

Washington Irving's first book, *A History of New York from the Beginning of the World to the End of the Dutch Dynasty* (1809) is a satire, presented as the work of a fictional character called Diedrich Knickerbocker. Through the years, the quaint and humorous Dutchman has become a familiar byword, particularly in New York.

Knickerbocker was later to decorate the Town Meeting plaque in 1971 and the Sebastian plaque in 1982 (SML 366). The Society will reissue the original Knickerbocker figurines to members-only in March, 1983, concluding the Washington Irving series. All six Society figurines will be permanently retired in August, 1983.

SML 143 Rip Van Winkle	1950 143 SR 1950–1975
SML 143-A Rip Van Winkle (*Society member*)	143-A LR Sept. 1, 1980 to Aug. 30, 1983
SML 144 Dame Van Winkle	144 SR 1950–1975
SML 144-A Dame Van Winkle (*Society member*)	144-A LR March 1, 1981 to Aug. 30, 1983

Rip and Dame Van Winkle appear in Washington Irving's tale *Rip Van Winkle* (1819), collected in his *Sketchbook of Geoffrey Crayon, Gent.* Henpecked Rip and his dog Wolf wander into the Catskill Mountains before the Revolutionary War. They join a group of dwarfs and Rip drinks from a keg. He awakens 20 years later, an old man. He returns to find Dame Van Winkle dead and the portrait of King George replaced by one of George Washington.

The newly formed Sebastian Society reissued Rip in September, 1980, and Dame in March, 1981, as member-only figurines. Both will be permanently retired in August, 1983.

SML 146 Tom Bowline, Ashore	1950 146 SR 1949–1975
	LR 1976–Present
	(No. 6246)
SML 146-A Tom Bowline, Penstand	146-A SR 1958–1967

Baston researched the costume and equipment for the Yankee Sea Captain (SML 132) in 1949. In 1950 he designed Tom Bowline, Ashore and Donald McKay at the Peabody Museum in Salem.

Tom Bowline (pronounced Bó'lin) was the common name for a common sailor. During the heights of New England's China trade, he was a familiar figure in the ports of Marblehead and Salem. Baston portrays him home from a long voyage with his duffle bag over his shoulder and his pet parrot dangling in a cage from his other hand.

SML 148 The Old Salt   1950 SR 1950–1975
                                              LR 1976–Present
                                              (No. 6242)

Baston designed two simple figurines in 1950 that were meant to be sold in gift shops as inexpensive tourist items. Old Salt, a New England fishing character, is shown dressed in oilskins mending a net. He sold in 1950 for $1.50.

SML 147 Donald McKay   1950 SR 1950–1975
                                              LR 1976–Present
                                              (No. 6249)

Donald McKay (1810–1880) is the third figure in Baston's China Trade series. McKay is portrayed in his Boston shipyard displaying the half-model of his first Yankee Clipper, *Staghound*. The model is mounted on an elaborate billethead. McKay is persuading financiers that a slender, fast ship will earn more money than a pot-bellied slow packet.

In 1869, his *Glory of the Seas* made a record run of 94 days from New York to San Francisco. He built several ships for the Union Navy during the Civil War.

SML 149 Cow Hand   1950 SR 1950–1975
                                              LR 1978–Present
                                              (No. 6508)

The Cow Hand is the other (along with The Old Salt) figurine designed to retail inexpensively. The figure at left, the Marblehead version, uses two shades of brown. When Baston reissued Cow Hand in 1978, he painted it more elaborately.

SML 150 Swan Boat   **1950 150 SR 1950–1975**
LR 1976–Present
(No. 6244)

SML 150-A Swan Boat—Masons   **150-A C 1961 250**

The R. H. Stearns department store was located facing the Boston Common, a large piece of land in downtown Boston originally used as a common feeding ground for the Colony's farmers and now a beautiful public park. At Stearns' request, Baston designed a Swan Boat, the small touring boat that carries the young of all ages on the Common Pond during the Summer.

Baston was delighted when Woody, aged five, sat in the right front seat and he modeled him wearing a captain's hat. In 1961, Baston produced 250 pieces for the Masons bearing the inscription "Grand Lodge of Masons in Massachusetts 1961." The Grand Lodge used the figurines as awards.

SML 151 The Town Crier   **1950 SR 1950–1975**
LR 1976–Present
(No. 6247)

In 1950, Baston removed the head of the Toll House Pilgrim man (SML 72), placed it on the body of the Toll House Town Crier (SML 92), and titled the figurine "The Town Crier." He sold it in his retail stores. The design was especially popular in Provincetown (on the tip of Cape Cod) where the town maintained a town crier up to modern times.

SML 152 Malvolio   **1950 SR 1950–1975**
SML 153 Countess Olivia

This pair, from Shakespeare's *Twelfth Night* (1600), represent some of the finest low comedy in Shakespeare. Malvolio is Olivia's steward. He is a pompous fool who secretly aspires to her love. Annoyed by his conceit, others concoct a scheme to turn Olivia against him. A letter is forged in her handwriting, leading him to believe she returns his love. He is conned into smiling continuously, wearing cross garters and yellow, the color she abhors. When Olivia shows astonishment at his absurd behavior, he keeps quoting parts of the letter until he is shut up in a dark room as a lunatic.

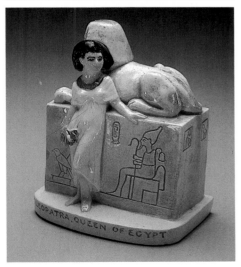

SML 154 Paul Revere	1950 154 SR 1950–1975
	LR 1976–Present
	(No. 6243)
SML 154-A Paul Revere—Masons	154-A C 1955 500

Baston designed Paul Revere, the Boston silversmith made famous for his ride to Lexington and Concord warning the Minutemen that "The British are coming," as an obvious Boston gift item. He took Brom Bones (SML 142) off his horse and seated Paul.

In 1955, he inscribed the figurine base with "Paul Revere Lodge A.F. & A.M. (Ancient Free and Accepted Masons) 100th Anniversary" and sold 500 to the lodge.

SML 155 Mark Antony	1950 155 SR 1950–1975
SML 156 Cleopatra (*Version I*)	156 SR 1950–1962
SML 156-A Cleopatra (*Version II*)	156-A SR 1963–1975

Baston created Shakespeare's lovers (*Antony and Cleopatra*, 1607) as part of his Shakespeare series. He put a Queen Nefertiti-type headdress on Cleopatra.

When the movie *Cleopatra* was released in 1963 amid great publicity and hoopla, Baston changed the Egyptian headwear with black hair as worn by Elizabeth Taylor in the movie.

SML 157 Touchstone, the Jester   1950 SR 1950–1975
SML 158 Audrey, A Country Wench

Baston chose these characters from *As You Like It* (1600) to conclude his Shakespearean series. Touchstone is a court jester, a witty and cynical fellow. His humor is realistic and biting and he openly insults his betrothed, Audrey, who is too stupid to realize it.

Audrey later appears with Davy Crockett in Pioneer Couple (SML 288).

SML 159 Andrew Jackson   1950 159 SR 1950–1975
      LR 1979–Present
      (No. 6011)
SML 159-A (*Penstand*)   159-A SR 1958–1967

Baston designed Andrew Jackson as part of his proposed Guggenheim fellowship series. The seventh president of the United States is shown in the uniform he wore when commanding at the battle of New Orleans. Lance discontinued production of the design in 1976 and then reissued it once again in 1979.

SML 160 Will Rogers   1950 SR 1950–1975
      LR 1979–Present
      (No. 6012)

Will Rogers (1879–1935) was an actor and humorist, widely popular for his vaudeville act of talking while twirling a lasso. He wrote a series of books and an extremely popular syndicated newspaper column on the news of the day. An early enthusiast for aviation, he was killed in an airplane accident while flying with the noted aviator Wiley Post.

Baston designed him for two reasons. He admired Rogers' thinking and writing and he wanted to create some figures that had broad geographical appeal.

SML 161 Motif No. 1   1950 161 SR 1950–1975
      LR 1976–Present
      (No. 6245)
SML 161-A "Rockport National Bank"   161-A C 1956 200
SML 161-B Penstand   161-B SR 1958–1960

The fish house in Rockport, Massachusetts is reputed to have been the source material for more paintings than any other building in the country. Baston designed it for sale in gift shops in Rockport, located a few miles from Marblehead.

In 1956, Baston received a commercial order for 200 pieces from the Rockport National Bank.

The building was destroyed in the East Coast blizzard of February, 1978, and Baston designed the Motif No. 1 plate (page 140) to help the Rockport Artists' League raise funds to restore the house. It has since been reconstructed and the original charm has been maintained.

SML 162 Cranberry Picker   1950 162 SR 1950–1975
                                         LR 1976–Present
                                         (No. 6248)
SML 162-A Blueberry Picker   162-A SR 1955–1957

Cranberries are one of Massachusetts' primary farm products. Baston designed a Cape Cod farm worker picking cranberries by the now obsolete hand scoop method.

For a few years, Baston changed the mold inscription to read "BLUEBERRY PICKER" and painted the berry tray blue. No more than 200 were produced.

SML 163 Phoebe—House of Seven Gables   1950 SR 1950–1975

The House of Seven Gables, inspiration for Nathaniel Hawthorne's novel, is located in Salem, adjacent to Marblehead. Following his 1948 House of Seven Gables design (SML 111), the House of Seven Gables Foundation, organized to maintain the building, requested that Baston design a series for sale to visitors. The results were Phoebe, Penny Shop, Judge Pyncheon and Holgrave.

Phoebe is the heroine of the novel. She rescues her relatives from their confusion and poverty and lifts a curse from the family. Of all the series designs, Phoebe was least in demand and, hence, rarest.

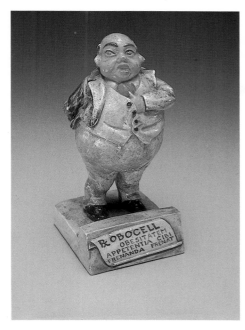

SML 164 Mr. Obocell   1950 C 1950–1964 45,000

Baston designed Mr. Obocell for the Irwin Neisler drug company. Obocell was a patent medicine for obesity, based on the theory of cutting down the taker's appetite. Mr. Obocell has become so bloated that, in bending over, the seat of his trousers has ripped. He has just discovered the damage.

Neisler salesmen gave the figurine to doctors, and over a many year period Baston produced 45,000 pieces. In 1956, Baston produced Mrs. Obocell (SML 268) as Obocell's companion.

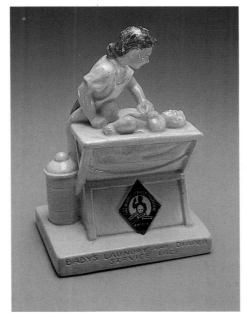

SML 165 National Diaper Service   1950 165 C 1950 2,000
SML 165-A Modern Mother   165-A SR 1951–1975

Art Ginnell of Marblehead, previously a halfback on the Fordham University "Seven Blocks of Granite" football team, ran the service. Baston produced 2,000 of these pieces which were given to customers and used in advertising by the company.

After the commercial contract had run out, Baston removed the logo and sold it to his stores as part of his Mother and Child series.

SML 166 Penny Shop—   1951 SR 1951–1975
    House of Seven Gables   LR 1976–Present
                                        (No. 6122)

A continuation of the House of Seven Gables series, Hepzibah Pyncheon is at the counter of her Penny Shop selling gingerbread to a neighborhood boy. The design was first sold through the House of Seven Gables and then sold through other retail stores.

SML 167 Judge Pyncheon   1951 SR 1951–1975

The villain of the House of Seven Gables is marching relentlessly toward the house which he intends to seize. Along with the House, Phoebe, Penny Shop, Holgrave and Nathaniel Hawthorne, the series sold continually from the early 1950's to 1975.

SML 168 Sebastian Dealer Plaque   1951 168 SR 1951–1975
    (*Marblehead*)
SML 168-A (*Hudson*)   168-A LR 1976–1978
SML 168-B (*U.S.A.*)   168-B LR 1979
SML 168-C (*New England*)   168-C LR 1980–1981

In 1951, Baston had stopped distributing Sebastians through Carbone and Schmid. Now selling through the Hunt local sales force (1951–1952), Baston designed a plaque advertising Sebastians and sold them to his dealers for display at their stores. The plaque was available up to his 1976 transition to Lance.

From 1976 to 1978, Sebastians were produced in Hudson, Massachusetts, and the plaque wording was so changed. In 1979, when the plant was opened in Lee, the words were changed to "U.S.A." and in 1980 and 1981, to "New England." On December 31, 1981, the plaque was changed from the 31-year-old Town Crier figure to Diedrich Knickerbocker (SML 366-A).

SML 169 The Madonna of the Goldfinch   1951 169 SR 1951–1975
                                      LR 1976–Present
                                      (No. 6312)
SML 169-A   169-A SR 1965–1973

Raphael's Madonna of the Goldfinch was painted during his Florentine Madonna period (1504–1508) and now hangs in the Vatican. The Madonna is with Jesus while John the Baptist pets a tiny Goldfinch.

Baston, along with his other Madonnas, also cast this miniature in a hard synthetic wood and sold a few hundred pieces.

SML 171 Sistine Madonna   1951 171 SR 1951–1975
                                     LR 1976–Present
                                     (No. 6313)
SML 171-A (*Synthetic Wood*)   171-A 1965–1973

The third and last of Baston's Raphael Madonnas, the Sistine Madonna was painted in Rome and now hangs in the Dresden Museum. Two hundred pieces were cast in hard synthetic wood and sold locally.

SML 170 Madonna of Chair   1951 170 SR 1951–1975
                                     LR 1976–Present
                                     (No. 6311)

SML 170-A (*Synthetic Wood*)   170-A SR 1965–1973

Baston created a series of three Madonnas from the great Madonna paintings of Raphael Sanzio (1483–1520). The Chair Madonna was painted during Raphael's Roman period and now hangs in the Pitti Palace in Florence.

Baston cast a few hundred of this Madonna in a hard synthetic wood base (illustrated with Our Lady of Good Voyage, SML 211) and sold them locally.

SML 172 Baby Buggy of 1850   1951 SR 1951–1975
                                     LR 1976–Present
                                     (No. 6303)

Baston researched this 1850's mother and her antique perambulator at the Ipswich Historical Society. In all of his period work, Baston has always used authentic wear and equipment based on museum and library research.

SML 174 The Weaver   1951 SR 1951–1975
                                                   LR 1976–Present
                                                   (No. 6302)

Baston designed a young mother at a loom being imitated by her son seated in a box which he conceives to be a loom. A Marblehead hand weaver supplied the old model.

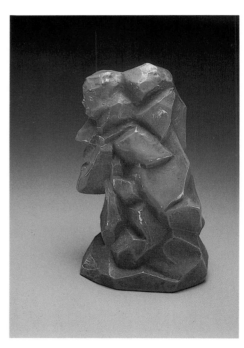

SML 173 Lacemaker   1951 173 SR 1951–1975
                                                   LR 1976–Present
                                                   (No. 6301)
SML 173-A Penstand   173-A SR 1958–1967
SML 173-B Gem Crib and Cradle Co.   173-B C 1953 2,500

While researching his Raphael Madonna series, Baston conceived of another Mother and Child series in historical treatment. He went to the Ipswich Historical Society in Ipswich, Massachusetts, for costume and cradle of this colonial mother.

In 1953, he added a Gem Crib and Cradle Co. identification and produced 2,500 pieces for Gem salesmen's use in furniture stores.

SML 175 Great Stone Face   1951 SR 1951–1975

A gift shop in Franconia, New Hampshire, requested a miniature version of New Hampshire's natural "Old Man of the Mountain." Baston sold them to White Mountain area tourist shops. The huge formation, jutting out of a cliff over a beautiful lake valley, has been the subject of a great deal of art and literature.

SML 176 Christopher Columbus   1951 SR 1951–1975

Baston designed America's discoverer as one of America's Famous Men. He has the Italian sailor authentically dressed, standing behind a ship's lantern on the *Santa Maria*.

SML 177 Sir Francis Drake   1951 SR 1951–1975

Drake (1540–1596) was the first Englishman to sail around the globe. Baston designed this miniature after one of the figureheads in the collection at the Marine Museum in Mystic, Connecticut. In all, about 500 were produced, including a few which were sold in a Montreal, Canada, gift store as a bust of William Shakespeare (!).

SML 178 Jesse Buffum   1951 178 C 1951 1,300
SML 178-A (*On Black Disc Base*)   178-A C 1951 200

Station WEEI was a popular showcase of Boston's 1950's, and many of its announcers were household names. In one contract, Baston designed seven of the most popular and produced 1,300 of each for sale and promotion by the station. Another 200 of each were mounted on a black base and used as special promotions by the station.

Jesse Buffum did the early morning farm show in a thick Maine drawl.

SML 179 Carl Moore   1951 179 C 1951 1,300
SML 179-A (*On Black Disc Base*)   179-A C 1951 200
SML 179-B (*The Piano Player*)   179-B SR 1953–1975
SML 179-C (*The Old Pro*)   179-C LR 1979–Present
                                                             (No. 6509)

Carl Moore was an announcer who played a studio piano and amazed telephone callers who tried to stump him on old songs and usually failed. Following the WEEI promotion, Baston renamed Moore "The Piano Player" and put him in the retail line.

Production was discontinued in 1976 and then Lance reintroduced him in July, 1979, as "The Old Pro."

Many have commented on the similarity between Moore at the piano and President Harry Truman. In 1953, Margaret Truman, Harry's daughter, appeared in a Marblehead summer theater show and Baston gave her a miniature of The Piano Player.

SML 180 Caroline Cabot   1951 180 C 1951 1,300
SML 180-A (*On Black Disc Base*)   180-A C 1951 200

Caroline Cabot, a WEEI announcer, was the home economics advisor and presented the daily consumer tips. She is reading from her list of do's and don'ts and is dressed in one of her famous hats.

SML 181 Mother Parker   1951 181 C 1951 1,300
SML 181-A (*On Black Disk Base*)   181-A C 1951 200

"Mother" Parker was the cooking editor, the Julia Childs of the 1950's when radio still was king (just barely). Baston portrayed her tossing a frenzied salad on a sadly wilting table.

SML 182 Charles Ashley   1951 182 C 1951 1,300
SML 182-A (*On Black Disc Base*)   182-A C 1951 200

Charles Ashley was the WEEI news editor. Baston portrayed him reading from a long teletype script. In 1951, he might be reading about President Truman firing General Douglas MacArthur during the height of the Korean War or Bobby Thomson's incredible last minute home run that won the playoff for the New York Giants in a last-day playoff against the Brooklyn Dodgers.

SML 183 E. B. Rideout   1951 183 C 1951 1,300
SML 183-A (*On Black Disc Base*)   183-A C 1951 200

E. B. Rideout was WEEI's weather forecaster. Since weather forecasting in 1951 was not the science it is today, the Boston coastal currents made E. B. the butt of many a joke. Baston portrayed him all dressed in a tight formal suit with his thermometer showing 120 degrees.

SML 184 Priscilla Fortescue   1951 184 C 1951 1,300
SML 184-A (*On Black Disc Base*)   184-A C 1951 200

Priscilla Fortescue was fashions editor for WEEI. Because of her well-known enthusiasm for camping and riding, Baston modeled her in a riding habit, standing in front of a log cabin and being gazed at admiringly by her horse.

SML 185 Chiquita Banana (*Version I*)   1951 C 1951 2,000

Chiquita Banana, the advertising symbol for United Fruit Company's banana brand, is a significant miniature in Sebastian history. The complex design and commercial approach gave Baston his introduction to New York City advertising agencies which were later to award him such commissions as Jell-O, *Reader's Digest*, Curtis Publishing, and Johnson & Johnson. With this job began his routine trips to Madison Avenue and nights in the Gramatan Hotel in Bronxville.

The figure's legs are so thin that the figurine had to be constructed and cast upside down. Due to the special requirements of the job, all features were handpainted by Baston personally.

SML 186 Chiquita Banana (*Version II*)   1951 C 1951 1,500

Following the shipment of the 2,000 Chiquitas on the first order, Baston changed the design for the second order. He added a palm tree to increase structural strength and simplify casting and packaging. As with the first version, Baston handpainted all the features personally.

SML 187 Chiquita Banana Ashtray   1951 C 1951 200

Baston designed an ashtray at the same time as the promotional figurines. Ceramastone is not a suitable material for functional usage, and the ashtrays were not popular. Production stopped at 200 pieces.

SML 188 MIT—1916 Seal   1951 188 C 1951 300
SML 188-A MIT—1952 Seal   188-A C 1951 500

An acquaintance commissioned Baston to design 300 MIT seals for his own graduating class and 500 for the upcoming 1952 class. The plaques were distributed to 300 alumni (1916) and 500 graduates during the June, 1952 commencement exercises.

SML 189 The Observer and   1951 C 1951 2,000
        Dame New England

1948's Jordan Marsh Observer (SML 113) leaves his position at the fence and is escorting Dame New England for this 1951 promotion by the Boston department store. Just as the Jordan Marsh promotions manager invented the "Observer" from all the sidewalk superintendents watching 1948 store construction, so too did he invent Dame New England. The couple was used in all store promotions.

SML 190 Jordan Observer   1951 C 1951 3,000
        Rides the Allied White Horse

Jordan Marsh is one of the Allied chain of stores. As part of a national promotion in 1951, the Boston store placed their Observer on one of "the Allied White Horses." In designing this miniature, Baston used the same horse he used in Brom Bones (SML 142) and Paul Revere (SML 152).

SML 191　The Iron Master's House　　　　1951 SR 1951–1955

Following the popularity of his House of Seven Gables (SML 111), Baston designed the home of the superintendent of the Iron Works in nearby Saugus, built in 1635. The house was not well known, and the design was discontinued in 1955 with only 200 sold.

SML 192　Chief Pontiac　　　　　　　1951 C 1951 250

Baston designed an Indian Chief with three-feather head-dress and bear-claw necklace for a regional Pontiac Motor Company promotion.

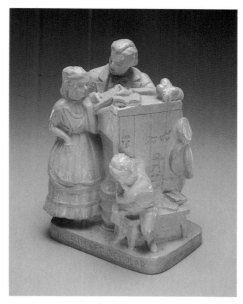

SML 193　The Favored Scholar　　　　1952 193 SR 1952–1957
SML 193-A (*Painted*)　　　　　　　193-A SR 1954–1957

Salem Sculptor John Rogers (1829–1904) created over a hundred designs cast into plaster sculpture. Known as "Rogers Groups," they are now cherished and valued art representing a history of America. Standing a foot to over two feet high, they are a tannish-brown in hue.

Baston chose three Rogers Groups on display at the Harrison Grey Otis House on Cambridge Street in Boston to reduce to miniature scale. About 500 of each were produced, but Sebastian collectors did not like the absence of color. About 50 of each were painted, but they were not modeled with color separation in mind.

"The Favored Scholar" shows a young man teacher at a high desk explaining some course of study to an attractive young lady student while a youthful male student tries to break up the conversation.

SML 194　Neighboring Pews　　　　1952 194 SR 1952–1957
SML 194-A (*Painted*)　　　　　　　194-A SR 1954–1957

One of the Rogers Groups (see SML 193), "Neighboring Pews" portrays a young man leaning over the pew in front of him to show an attractive lady the hymn number. He is inadvertently jostling a less attractive elderly lady in the process. Meanwhile, a youngster in cocked hat in the pew in front snoozes through the entire proceedings.

SML 195 Weighing the Baby　　　1952 195 SR 1952–1957
SML 195-A (*Painted*)　　　　　　195-A SR 1954–1957

Third in the Rogers series (see SML 193), "Weighing the Baby" portrays a young mother who has brought her baby to the grocery store to be weighed. She and the grocer are astonished at the infant's progress. They do not see the baby's brother pulling a corner of the blanket and tipping the scales several pounds.

SML 196 The First House,　　　　1952 SR 1952–1975
　　　　Plimoth Plantation

This is a miniature of the original houses built by the earliest settlers of New England in the 1600's. Baston originally produced it for Smith News, a gift outlet in Plymouth, Massachusetts, site of the original Puritan settlement. A year later Baston used the same house to create his PIONEER VILLAGE (SML 219).

SML 197 Benjamin Franklin　　　1952 197 SR 1952–1975
　　　　　　　　　　　　　　　　　LR 1976–Present
　　　　　　　　　　　　　　　　　(No. 6006)
SML 197-A (*Penstand*)　　　　197-A SR 1958–1967
SML 197-B (*Curtis Plan Representative*)　197-B C 1953 1,800
SML 197-C (*Keystone Readers' Service*)　197-C C 1955 2,500

Baston first designed Franklin as one of his Favorite Americans series for his retail stores. A year after it was produced, Baston was commissioned to create a special piece with a penstand base inscribed "Compliments—Curtis Plan Representative." It was used by Curtis salesmen (*Saturday Evening Post* and other magazines) to promote sales.

The Franklin and *Post* tie-in continued in 1955 with the Keystone Readers' Service figurine (reads "Ben Franklin Award—Keystone Readers' Service" in heavy base), also used in Curtis promotions.

SML 198 Colonial Kitchen   1952 SR 1952–1975
LR 1976–Present
(No. 6251)

When Baston researched the Iron Master's House in Saugus (SML 191), he sketched the details of the interior. A year later he produced Colonial Kitchen, the fireplace in the Saugus kitchen. The house was not a popular item but the kitchen sold steadily with Lance continuing it in production.

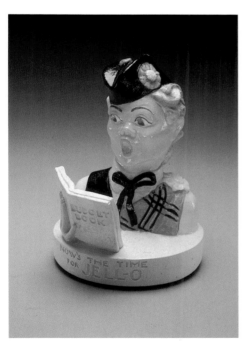

SML 199 Scottish Girl (*Jell-O*)   1952 C 1952 3,000

Following the success with Baston's Chiquita Banana promotion, the New York advertising agency of Young & Rubicam planned an advertising program for General Foods' Jell-O brand that involved a series of 13 Sebastians over the next five years (1952–1956). When Jell-O ran an ad showing a Scottish girl studying her budget, the headline said, "Now's the Time for Jell-O." Before the ad appeared nationally, Jell-O sent Sebastians to its top 3,000 national accounts reminding them ". . . when you see this lass in your magazines and newspapers, remember how Jell-O is helping you sell. Stock up now!" This was followed a few months later with "Lost in the Kitchen," "The Fat Man," etc., all warning that "Now's the Time for Jell-O."

Baston worked continuously with Young & Rubicam and General Foods in their old New York City Postum Building office until the series was completed. The *Reader's Digest* office was also located there.

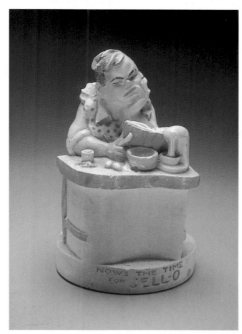

SML 200 Lost in the Kitchen (*Jell-O*)   1952 C 1952 3,000

The 1952 Jell-O ad reads: "Having a little trouble, Mac? Buck Up! You still can surprise the little woman and the kids with a swell Jell-O gelatin dessert! It's an absolute cinch to make...and we guarantee they'll love every bit of it! Now's the time for Jell-O!" (This obviously was before McDonald's!).

SML 201 The Fat Man (*Jell-O*)   1952 C 1952 3,000

Number three in the Jell-O series (SML199), this slightly paunchy hero stares at his bathroom scale. The ad reads: "Whoops! Putting on a little weight, eh? Now's the time for low-calorie, grand-tasting Jell-O!"

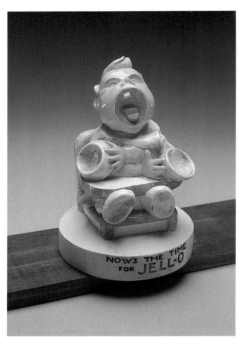

SML 202 Baby (*Jell-O*)   1952 C 1952 3,000

The fourth in the Jell-O series (see SML 199), a nasty, one-toothed infant rebels against his standard baby food. The 1952 ad reads: "Hey, take it easy, Junior! Here comes a big dish of shining, shimmering, grand-tasting, good-for-you Jell-O! That ought to keep you happy!"

In the photo, the BABY is mounted to one of Baston's display racks that he carried with him when selling Sebastians to prospective clients.

SML 203 Stork (*Jell-O*)   1952 C 1952 3,000

Finishing the year with another budget theme (see SML 199), this fifth Jell-O piece informs us we can still be economical with our food money even in the face of a disaster. When triplets arrive, Now's the Time for Jell-O!

SML 204 Tabasco Sauce   1952 C 1952 1,000

A New York advertising agency gave Baston a contract to produce 1,000 Tabasco Sauce miniatures for use in a promotional giveaway. A small Tabasco Sauce sample bottle fits into the recess in the base. Advertising "Wake Up Food Flavors," the Spanish fellow in the rear is taking his Siesta. The man in front, having had a taste of tabasco, is not only awake but dancing.

SML 205 Aerial Tramway (*Version I*)   1952 C 1952 200
SML 206 Aerial Tramway (*Version II*)   C 1952 2,000

Baston designed an aerial tramway miniature for the State of New Hampshire Recreational Service for their use in promoting the ski trade. His first design (pictured at right) was a complicated design using thread as cables. The piece was popular, and when large orders came in, Baston modified the design (left) for large production and economy.

SML 207 Marblehead High   1952 C 1952 500
       School Plaque

Baston rarely refused a request from local organizations. When Marblehead High School asked for a quantity of plaques for use as handouts and awards, Baston recreated the town seal on a shield. The theme of the town, incorporated in 1649, is the seaman and Marblehead's ever-present sea.

SML 208 Emlyn Williams   1952 208 C 1952 200
       as Charles Dickens
SML 208-A Charles Dickens   208-A SR 1954–1975
                       LR 1976–Present
                       (No. 6117)

Emlyn Williams, noted Welsh actor, toured the United States in 1952 and 1953 recreating Charles Dickens reading from his own works. Baston created 200 "Emlyn Williams as Charles Dickens" miniatures for the Sol Hurok organization which used them as gifts to drama critics in the cities where Williams was to appear. Two years later, Baston dropped the "Emlyn Williams" from the base and Charles Dickens joined his family of characters in Baston's retail series.

SML 209 St. Jean d'Arc   1952 209 C 1952 1,200
       (*Square Base*)
SML 209-A Saint Joan of Arc   209-A SR 1954–1975
       (*Painted*)
SML 209-B Saint Joan of Arc   209-B SR 1954–1975
       (*Bronzed*)

Bishop Wright, head of the Worcester, Massachusetts, diocese, had a special interest in Joan of Arc. Baston designed a square-based figurine with "St. Jean d'Arc" cast in the base and the Bishop distributed 1,200 to selected parishioners. Two years later Baston rounded the base, Anglicized her name and distributed the miniature through his stores.

The *fleur-de-lis* pattern on her armor was difficult and expensive to paint. Baston tried to sell a bronzed, less expensive version, but sales of the unpainted version were always low.

SML 210 Saint Sebastian (*Painted*)   1952 210 C & SR 1952–1975
SML 210-A (*Ivory*)   210-A, B & C SR 1956–1975
SML 210-B (*Bronze*)
SML 210-C (*Wood*)

The St. Sebastian School in Newton, Massachusetts, commissioned Baston to design and produce a St. Sebastian figurine to be used as an award and fund-raiser. Four years later he placed the figurine in the retail line without changing anything from the Commercial design. St. Sebastian is the patron saint of soldiers and athletes and is portrayed as a warrior.

As with Saint Joan of Arc, Baston used a variety of materials and color (ivory and bronzed Ceramastone and a hard artificial wood resin) to make the piece easier to make and less expensive. The painted version remained the most popular.

SML 211 Our Lady of Good Voyage   1952 211 C & SR 1952–1975
SML 211-A (*Gold Finish*)   211-A, B & C SR 1956–1975
SML 211-B (*Wood*)
SML 211-C (*Ivory*)

The Roman Catholic Church of Gloucester, Massachusetts, requested this traditional Portugese Madonna for distribution to its parishioners. Many were carried in fishing vessels by members of the local fleet.

In 1956, Baston began distributing the piece through his retail stores. As with St. Joan and St. Sebastian, he tried to lower time and price by gold- and ivory-finishing the piece or casting it in an artificial wood (see SML 169), but the painted pieces remained the most popular.

SML 212 Old Powder House   1952 212 C 1952 500
    (*Somerville Nat'l Bank*)
SML 212-A (*Somerville Bank Penstand*) 212-A C 1952 500
SML 212-B (*Mayor Brennan*)   212-B C 1954 400
SML 212-C Old Powder House—1775 212-C SR 1954–1975
SML 212-D (*Penstand*)   212-D SR 1958–1967

Somerville National Bank, in a suburb of Boston, commissioned Baston to design a miniature and penstand inscribed "Somerville National Bank" and depicting the town's landmark, the Old Powder House (used to store gunpowder by the Colonists). He made 500 of each. Two years later, Mayor Brennan, running for reelection in Somerville, ordered 400 with his name inscribed. Beginning in 1954, Baston supplied them as figurines and penstands to his stores, but they were slow sellers outside of Somerville.

SML 213 Little Mother   1953 SR 1953–1975
              LR 1976–Present
              (No. 6231)

The *Godey's Lady's Book* was the first successful woman's magazine. The magazine, which featured articles by famous authors and colored plates of the latest fashions, attained a circulation of 150,000 by 1858 and was considered the standard for morals and good taste. When Baston planned a series of children for his retail stores he researched the Godey's Lady's Books on file at the Essex Institute in Salem. He advertised the line as "Victorian Children from Godey's Lady's Book Story Series," and it has remained the top selling line of all Sebastian

Miniatures. The slightly larger scale of the Godey children than the rest of the miniatures is due to Baston's plan to have them compete with Hummel figurines.

The rocker in Little Mother is the family chair and Baston grew up with it. It now resides in Woody's Wayland home and was used in 1981's Family Reading (SML 387). In 1982, Baston designed a bas relief of Little Mother for the third plate in his "There Was a Time" series (see page 140).

SML 214 Ride to the Hounds   1953 214 SR 1953–1975
                   LR 1977–Present
                   (No. 6234)
SML 214-A Cavalry   214-A SR 1961–1965

Ride to the Hounds is the second Godey child. In 1961, Baston changed the boy's cap to a Union uniform cap, the uniform to blue and the horse from spotted to brown and renamed him "Cavalry." He was sold as a pair with Parade Rest (SML 216) during our Civil War Centennial.

SML 215 Switching the Freight   1953 SR 1953–1975
                                        LR 1977–Present
                                        (No. 6236)

"Switching the Freight," third in the Godey Children series (see SML 213), was modeled after Baston had watched his son Woody play with his toy trains in Marblehead.

SML 216 Parade Rest   1953 SR 1953–1975
                                  LR 1977–Present
                                  (No. 6233)

The fourth in the Godey series (see SML 213), this little boy is dressed in the Civil War uniform of a Zouave soldier. He was sold as a pair with "Cavalry" (SML 214-A) during our Civil War Centennial. In 1968, Baston converted him to a Drummer Boy (SML 362).

SML 217 Games in Springtime   1953 SR 1953–1975
                                      LR 1977–Present

The fifth in the Godey series (see SML 213), the little girl has just finished rolling her hoop and is considering the next hill.

SML 218 Speak For It   1955 SR 1953–1975
                                   LR 1977–Present
                                   (No. 6235)

The sixth and last of 1953's Godey Children series (see SML 213), a young lady dressed in an overstated and stiff child's costume of the 1850's tempts her dog with a morsel.

SML 219 Pioneer Village   1953 SR 1953–1975
                                                   LR 1976–Present
                                                      (No. 6252)

When a Salem gift shop asked Baston to design a typical
Salem colonial building, he took the house from Plymouth's
First House (SML 196), set it sideways on the base and added a
stock and pillory. The design remained a popular New England
tourist item.

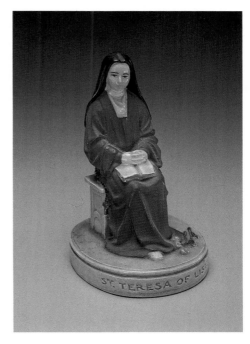

SML 220 Holgrave the Daguerrotypist   1953 SR 1953–1975

Holgrave is the last of the House of Seven Gables characters
(see SML 163). In Hawthorne's novel, the professional photographer is the hero whose strength of character lifts the curse
from the Pyncheon household.

SML 221 St. Teresa of Lisieux   1953 221 SR 1953–1975
SML 221-A (*Penstand*)   221-A SR 1958–1967

St. Teresa (or Theresa), a French Carmelite nun, is one of the
most widely loved saints of the Roman Catholic Church. Born
in 1873 and dead in 1897 at the age of 24, she was canonized in
1925, just 28 years after her death. Her spiritual autobiography,
written before her death, remains one of the most widely read
testaments to faith. Lisieux, France, home of her monastery, is
the scene of constant pilgrimages by the faithful.

Baston was asked to do a St. Teresa by the Carmelite order of
nuns in Danvers, Massachusetts. He sold the miniatures
through his stores and the design was distributed through
Catholic religious stores.

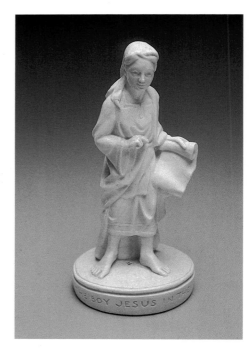

SML 222 Darned Well He Can	1953 222 SR 1953–1956
SML 222-A Boy and Pelican	222-A 1956–1975
	1978–Present
	(No. 6228)

At the request of a Florida gift shop, Baston designed a Negro boy and pelican sitting on the piles of a Florida harbor. The bird is looking intently at the catch. Baston named the piece after the poem: "An amazing bird is the pelican, his mouth can hold more than his bellican."

After four years, Baston changed the confusing name and painted the lad white. It has remained in the line to the present time.

SML 224 Boy Jesus in the Temple	1953 224 C 1953 400
(*Painted*)	
SML 224-A (*Bronzed*)	224-A C 1953 100
SML 224-B (*White Marble*)	224-B C 1953 100

Cardinal Cushing directed the archdiocese to focus fund-raising activities on the Children's Home of Nazareth. Working through diocesan offices, Baston designed a figure of Jesus as a boy talking to the temple elders. In all, three production versions (painted, bronzed and white) were used for different activities.

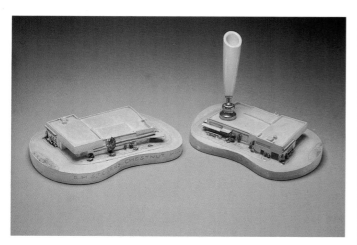

| SML 223 R. H. Stearns Chestnut Hill Mall | 1953 223 C 1953 1,500 |
| SML 223-A (*Penstand*) | 223-A C 1953 500 |

The R. H. Stearns Company opened a large store at a large new mall in Chestnut Hill (a Boston suburb) in 1953. To promote the opening, Baston designed a miniature and a penstand. Neither piece has any Baston or Sebastian identification.

| SML 225 Blessed Julie Billiart | 1952 C 1953 800 |

Sister Julie Billiart was the founder of the Notre Dame order of teaching nuns. The miniature was commissioned for school fund-raising. Baston's model was a larger bronze statue portraying Sister Billiart in her religious robes with a young girl standing beside her.

SML 226 "Old Put" Enjoys   1953 C & SR 1953–1956
        a Licking at Bunker Hill

The Putnam Pantry Candy Company was run by direct descendants of General Israel Putnam (1718–1790) of Bunker Hill battle fame. They requested Baston do a version of their ancestor for company advertising and also for sale by the company. Baston portrayed the General leaning against the Bunker Hill monument and licking out the inside of a chocolate kettle. The highly specialized design was a slow seller and was discontinued in 1956.

SML 228 The Schoolboy of 1850   1953 228 C 1953 100
SML 228-A *(Bronzed)*   228-A C 1953 500

In 1953, the town of Ashburnham, Massachusetts' Service Committee wished to raise funds to help their local servicemen during the Korean War. Baston and the committee decided on a miniature replica of the bronze statue on the campus of nearby Cushing Academy. He painted 100 and bronzed 500.

SML 227 Lion *(Jell-O)*   1953 C 1953 3,000

The sixth in the Jell-O series (see SML 199), this miniature reflects the change in Young & Rubicam's advertising direction. While the first five were headlined "Now's the Time for Jell-O," the Lion begins a series of individual ads. This one says: "Everyone Roars for Jell-O."

SML 229 Whale (*Jell-O*)   1954 C 1954 3,000

The seventh in the Jell-O series (see SML 199), this whale is looking for "A Whale of a Dessert." The 1954 ad says: "When I'm eating Jell-O, I wish I were a whale ... because then I'd be able to eat the most Jell-O in the whole world (and Jell-O's such a whale of a buy!)."

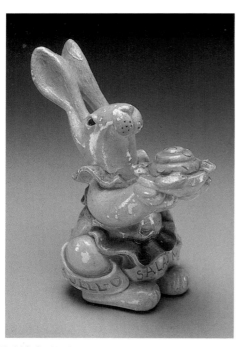

SML 230 Rabbit (*Jell-O*)   1954 C 1954 3,000

The eighth of the Jell-O series (see SML 199), this fellow tells us "A Jell-O Salad Makes the Meal." He obligingly offers his rabbit food.

SML 231 Moose (*Jell-O*)   1954 C 1954 3,000

The ninth Jell-O figurine, a stuffed moose is hanging from the wall over the fireplace and his paws rest easily on the mantle bracketing a dish of Jell-O and a spoon. Four different flavors perch in his antlers.

SML 232 The Old Covered Bridge   1954 SR 1954–1975
                                             LR 1976–Present
                                             (No. 6253)

In another traditional New England scene for the retail line, Baston portrayed two river banks and a red bridge spanning them over a rocky river basin. A horse-drawn carriage emerges from the bridge.

SML 233 The Nativity 1954 SR 1954–1975
LR 1976–Present
(No. 6314)

Plummer's, a fine china and glass store in Manhattan, asked Baston to design a highly miniaturized nativity scene for use on an expensive music box and also as an independent figurine. Baston conceived of an entire grouping of manger, holy family, wisemen, shepherds and animals under a green bower. The result, a masterpiece of miniature composition and detail, was the Sebastian Miniature Nativity.

In 1961, Baston broke up the separate design elements and cast them in three individual groupings, Manger (SML 323), The Wisemen (SML 324) and Shepherds (SML 325).

SML 234 Scuba Diver 1954 SR 1954–1956

One of Baston's Marblehead friends had another friend whose son had suffered psychological damage during the Korean War. Baston employed the young boy at the studio to assist in his recovery. He had been a scuba diver and began asking Baston to do a scuba diver in miniature. Scuba diving had not been popularized yet (TV's "Sea Hunt" and "Aquanauts" were still years away) and the piece sold poorly until discontinued in 1956. After working awhile in the studio, the boy recovered nicely and moved on.

SML 235 Stimalose 1954 C 1954 1,000

The Irwin Neisler Drug Company introduced a medicine with the tradename "Stimalose." The company advertised that just a few tablets would cure logginess caused by overeating or drinking too much. Baston portrayed a double bust of a depressed and a joyous person and produced 1,000 bronzed figurines for distribution by Neisler salesmen.

SML 236 Bluebird Girl 1954 C 1954 1,500

The man who supervised the Howard Johnson Pieman in 1947 requested that Baston create three miniatures for use in fund-raising for the Campfire Girls of America. These designs were discontinued after one year because the dress lengths were fluctuating so widely in the 1950's that current molds rapidly became obsolete.

A Bluebird Girl is shown patting the head of a huge inflated bluebird.

SML 237 Campfire Girl   1954 C 1954 2,500

The Campfire membership is the largest group of the three (Bluebird and Horizon). This girl is standing next to a fireplace with the Campfire Girl emblem on it. As with the other two in the series, this design was discontinued in 1954.

SML 238 Horizon Girl   1954 C 1954 1,000

Horizon Girls are the adult members of the Campfire Girl organization. Baston portrayed this girl as "ready to follow the Campfire teachings in her adult life."

SML 239 Kernel-Fresh Ashtray   1954 C 1954 500

While working on his Jell-O series, Baston created another piece for General Foods. Kernel-Fresh, the tradename for a line of packaged nuts, symbolized a Grenadier guard with a wheelbarrow load of mixed nuts. Baston mounted the white figure on a white ashtray and, like his Chiquita Banana ashtray (SML 187), experienced a weak reception.

SML 240 William Penn   1954 C 1954–1976 2,000

William Penn was made for the Penn Mutual Life Insurance Company in Philadelphia. A miniature replica of a large bronze statue, the miniature was distributed exclusively by the company president. The bronze statue was visible from his office.

The company purchased small quantities at various time intervals over the years and Lance produced the last quantity of 500 after the Marblehead studio was closed, a similar situation to the Shawmut Indian (SML 93).

SML 241 St. Pius   1954 C 1954 1,400
      (*Pope Pius X*)

Guiseppe Sarto (1835–1914) was named Pope Pius X in 1903. Known for his interest in the poor, he was canonized by Pius XII in 1954. Baston designed this miniature for the Archdiocese of Boston from a statue in the Holy Cross cathedral in Worcester, Massachusetts. It was used to commemorate Pius's canonization to sainthood.

SML 242 Resolute Insurance   1954 242 C 1954 800
         Company Clipper
SML 242-A Yankee Clipper Ship   242-A SR 1955–1975
                                           LR 1976–Present
                                           (No. 6254)
SML 242-B (*Penstand*)   242-B SR 1958–1967
SML 242-C (*Salem-Marblehead*   242-C C 1957–1965 50
         Rotary Club)

Baston designed a Yankee Clipper Ship for the Resolute Insurance Company. A year later he replaced the Resolute name with "Yankee Clipper" and distributed it through his stores. In 1957, he was asked to create a gift for Salem and Marblehead Rotary guest speakers so he cast the club titles into the base as special awards.

SML 243 Dachshund (*Audiovox*)   1954 C 1954 500
                                           SR 1955–1959

Baston created a dachshund listening with his head cocked on speculation for the Audiovox hearing aid company. The company ordered 500 and then Baston converted it to his retail line distribution with no design changes. It was a slow seller for a few years and then was discontinued.

SML 244 Our Lady of LaLeche   1954 SR 1954–1956 800

The Mission of Nombre de Dios in St. Augustine, Florida wrote Baston with a photo of the statue of Our Lady of LaLeche in their mission courtyard. He created 800 miniature replicas, 500 for the mission and 300 on speculation for his own stores.

(*Author's note:* In 1981, the author received a telephone call from the mission gift shop manager attempting, 27 years later, to place an order for another 100 pieces. I told her the miniatures were now selling at auctions for over $150. She said the original price for 500 miniatures was $1.75 each!)

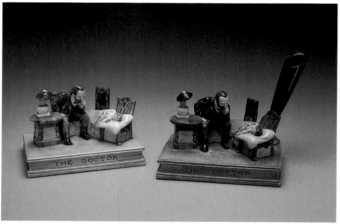

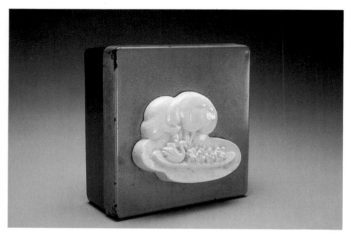

SML 245 The Doctor	1954 245 C 1954–1959 10,000		
(*Irwin Neisler; Paperweight*)			
SML 245-A (*Irwin Neisler Penstand*)	245-A C 1958–1960 2,000		
SML 245-B (*Figurine Base*)	245-B SR 1960–1975		
	LR 1976–Present		
	(No. 6214)		
SML 245-C (*Penstand*)	245-C SR 1960–1967		

The Irwin Neisler Drug Company commissioned Baston to produce a miniature derived from the painting by Sir Luke Fildes. 10,000 were used by Neisler salesmen as a handout to doctors and pharmacists, along with an additional 2,000 in penstand form. In 1960, Baston converted the Neisler commercial wording to "The Doctor" and supplied it in his retail line in figurine and penstand form.

SML 246 Swanboat Brooch—Empty Seats	1954 246 C 1954 500		
SML 247 Swan Boat Brooch—Full Seats	247 C 1954 500		
SML 247-A Swan Boat Gift Box	247-A C 1966 300		

Boston television station WBZ requested a set of miniature bas relief swan boats (see SML 150) as gifts for guests on a morning talk show. An empty-seat brooch was presented before the show and a full-seat version when the show was over.

In 1966, Baston's sister-in-law, Marion Keyes, retired from the Newton (Massachusetts) school system. He produced 300 plastic full-seat brooches from the 1954 molds and distributed 300 gift boxes at the retirement party.

SML 248 Dachshund   1955 248 SR 1955–1975
SML 248-A (*Bronzed*)   248-A 1955–1959

Baston made a sale of 1,000 figurines of a purebred dach-shund to a dog food firm. A Sebastian salesman persuaded him that he could sell more than 1,000 through his stores. Baston issued a painted and bronzed version to his stores and "I doubt if we sold 250 in all those years."

SML 249 Davy Crockett   1955 SR 1955–1975

On December 15, 1954, Walt Disney aired "Davy Crockett, Indian Fighter," on television (followed by "Davy Crockett Goes to Congress," January 26, 1955 and "Davy Crockett at the Alamo," February 23, 1955). The series, starring Fess Parker, created a national sensation. Baston responded early in 1955 by introducing a Davy Crockett figurine. The figure was later to appear in "Pioneer Couple" (SML 288) along with 1950's Shake-spearean "Audrey" (SML 158).

SML 250 Giraffe (*Jell-O*)   1955 C 1955 3,000

The tenth Jell-O figurine (see SML 199), a giraffe reaches for a serving of the dessert in the top branches of an African tree. Not only he but "Everyone Reaches for Jell-O."

SML 251 Old Woman in the Shoe (*Jell-O*)   1955 C 1955 3,000

In this eleventh Jell-O figurine (see SML 199), Baston squeezed 15 tiny people (eight standing, three in shoe windows and four on the ladder) onto a small-sized shoe. The top child is eating Jell-O with a huge spoon and the scene says: "Kids Love Jell-O."

SML 252 Santa (*Jell-O*)　　　　　1955 C 1955 3,000

The twelfth and next-to-last Jell-O figure (see SML 199), this Christmas ad inspired a wealth of miniature detail. Santa has just come down the chimney and finds a large serving of Jell-O waiting for him. The boy who prepared it is fast asleep under the table as is the tiny mouse tucked in his bed on the right side of the fireplace mantle. "Jell-O! A Fine Treat for All!"

SML 253-D The Man at the Wheel　　253-D C 1967 200
　　　　(*Gorton's*)

Captain Doliber was a Marblehead sailing captain. Another Marblehead yachtsman remodeled an America's Cup defender and the yacht was used by his family for several years. Both Doliber and the yacht were famous in Marblehead circles, and Baston produced 100 painted pieces for the Eastern Yacht Club and another 20 bronze pieces for the Foster family. In 1966, Baston modified the figure for sale through his stores as "The Skipper," both painted and bronzed. Finally, in 1967, Baston further modified the figure to "The Man at the Wheel" for Gorton's of Gloucester, a seafood processing company. They used 200 pieces in a promotion.

SML 253 Captain Doliber (*Painted*)　　1955 253 C 1955 100
SML 253-A (*Bronzed*)　　　　　　　253-A C 1955 20
SML 253-B The Skipper (*Painted*)　　253-B SR 1966–1975
　　　　　　　　　　　　　　　　　　LR 1976–Present
　　　　　　　　　　　　　　　　　　(No. 6256)
SML 253-C (*Bronzed*)　　　　　　　253-C SR 1966–1975

SML 254 Second Bank—State Street　　1955 254 C 1955 200
　　　　Trust Co. (*Penstand*)

SML 254-A (*Plaque*)   254-A C 1956 500

Boston's State Street Trust and Second Bank merged in the early 1950's. The seal shows the old State House, the symbol for the State Street Trust, superimposed on a large numeral "2." The penstand version was superseded by the less expensive plaque a year later.

SML 255 Horse Head (*Penstand*)   1955 255 SR 1955–1965
SML 255-A (*Bronzed*)   255-A SR 1957–1965

Baston designed a thoroughbred horse head for a specific horse show where they were used for awards. He placed it in his retail line, and a painted and bronzed version sold in quantities of a few hundred pieces total.

SML 256 Robin Hood and Little John   1956 C 1956 500

"The Adventures of Robin Hood" ran on television from September, 1955 to September, 1958. Starring Richard Greene, the show was sponsored by Johnson & Johnson, the New Jersey pharmaceutical and tape company. In the first of several commissions for this company, Baston designed Robin and Little John jousting on a crude bridge over a stream. The inscription reads: "Johnson & Johnson, Makers of Bandaid—Sponsors of Robin Hood T.V." and was distributed by Johnson & Johnson salesmen.

A second design portraying Little John presiding over the vanquished Robin in the water was never used.

SML 257 Robin Hood and Friar Tuck   1956 C 1956 500

As a followup to the Little John figurine, Baston designed a Robin Hood-Friar Tuck miniature. The base is inscribed "Robin Hood T.V. —Johnson & Johnson; Friar Tuck Carries Robin Hood Over the Stream."

SML 259 Three Little Kittens (*Jell-O*)   1956 C 1956 3,000

The Three Little Kittens are the thirteenth and final figurine in the Jell-O series (see SML 199). The three, all eating their Jell-O, proclaim: "Mother Dear! See Here, See Here!" All good children eat their Jell-O.

In all, Baston created thirteen designs and 39,000 figurines from 1953 to 1956. As today's collectors can testify, the Jell-O series remains a high-point in the history of Sebastian Miniature collecting.

SML 258 77th Bengal Lancer (*Jell-O*)   1956 258 C 1956 12
SML 258-A Royal Bengal Lancer   258-A SR 1956–1958

In 1956, Jell-O was planning the sponsorship of a television program featuring the 77th Bengal Lancers. Because of his relationship with Jell-O on the 1952–1956 series, Baston designed a Jell-O 77th Lancer bas relief figurine and cast and painted a dozen figurines on speculation. General Foods did not go ahead with the promotion and Baston removed the "Jell-O" name for distribution through his retail stores. It was a very slow seller and he discontinued it a few years later.

SML 260 Texcel Tape Boy   1956 C 1956 2,000

Baston produced seven designs for Johnson & Johnson in 1956. The "Texcel Tape Boy" was the third. The base is inscribed: (Front: "Texcel® Cellophane Tape"; Rear: "Permacel Tape Corporation, New Brunswick, N.J. A Johnson & Johnson Company."

The 2,000 were used by Johnson & Johnson salesmen to introduce their new cellophane tape, designed to compete with 3M's Scotch-brand.

SML 261 Permacel Tower of Tape (*Ashtray*)   1956 C 1956 500

This fourth 1956 Johnson & Johnson figurine portrays a tower of Permacel tapes showing all the tapes they supplied. The tower is poised next to a recess that holds a small glass ashtray. The piece was used for promotional purposes and was accompanied by a brochure describing the variety of Permacel tape applications.

In an excess of corporate zeal, Johnson & Johnson shipped Baston a wealth of Permacel tapes to use as "models." Baston says, "We had them around the house for years. Woody even used them to wrap around hockey sticks and footballs."

SML 262 Arthritic Hands (*Johnson & Johnson*)   1956 C 1956 400

In his seventh and final 1956 Johnson & Johnson design, Baston modified Durer's "Praying Hands" (SML 264) into a pair of hands crippled with arthritis. The piece was used in a promotion for a Johnson & Johnson drug that eased the pain of arthritis.

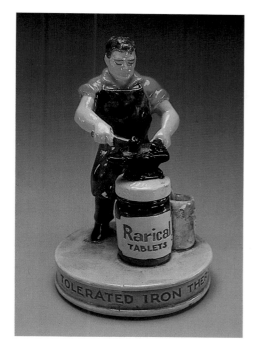

SML 263 Rarical Blacksmith   1956 263 C 1956 1,500
SML 263-A A Colonial Blacksmith   263-A SR 1968–1975
                                                          LR 1976–Present
                                                            (No. 6219)

The fifth 1956 Johnson & Johnson commission, this one advertises RARICAL, the brandname for their iron fortifier food supplement. The design was changed in 1968 from a Rarical bottle to a tree stump and distributed through the retail stores.

The Rarical version was distributed by Johnson & Johnson salesmen to pharmacists.

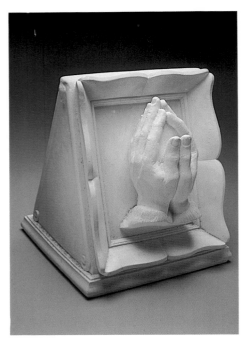

SML 265 Eastern Paper Plaque   1956 C 1956 200

This simple logotype plaque was made for the Eastern Paper Manufacturer's Association for distribution at a 1956 convention. A three-dimensional version of their trademark, the scroll is inscribed "Atlantic Eastern & Manifest."

SML 266 Girl on Diving Board   1956 C 1956 300
      (*King George Hotel*)

The King George Hotel in Brooklyn advertised "The World's Largest Indoor Swimming Pool" to various New York City convention agencies. The figurine was mailed to these agencies and certain large companies in the Manhattan-Brooklyn area.

SML 264 Praying Hands Frame   1956 264 C 1956 700
SML 264-A (*Bronzed Figurine*)   264-A SR 1957–1965

In his sixth 1956 Johnson & Johnson design, Baston portrayed Albrecht Durer's drawing of praying hands framed in an easel-type frame. The design was commissioned to introduce a tranquilizer, and the back of the frame displayed capsules and tablets painted the color of the drugs. A total of 700 were distributed to doctors and pharmacists by Johnson & Johnson salesmen.

A year later, Baston removed the commercial frame and distributed the bronzed hands through his retail group, primarily religious stores.

SML 267 Elsie the Cow Billboard   1956 C 1956 1,000

Baston designed Borden's Elsie the Cow standing next to a blank billboard. The Borden Company purchased 1,000 of these plaques over a one-year period. They were supplied blanks and various messages were painted on them by the company for a special communique or promotion.

SML 268 Mrs. Obocell   1956 C 1956–1964 2,000

Following 1950's ongoing and highly successful Mr. Obocell promotion (SML 164), Baston designed his mate, the corpulent Mrs. Obocell. She was not as popular as the man, and Baston produced only 2,000 pieces over the life of the promotion. Both pieces were produced for Irwin Neisler.

SML 269 Twins (*Mead-Johnson*)   1956 269 C 1956 700
SML 269-A Nurse   269-A SR 1967–1975
                                              LR 1976–Present
                                              (No. 6212)

Baston designed a young mother holding her twins, one sleeping and the other lively. The figurine was used as a promotion for one of Mead-Johnson's baby products and the base read: "Alike, But Oh So Different!" Baston made a four-foot-high version for use at trade shows. The mold was built into a metal barrel to contain the weight and almost one hundred pours were required to complete the sculpture. The finished statue was shipped in wooden crates all around the country.

In 1967, Baston added a nurse's cap and titled the miniature "Nurse."

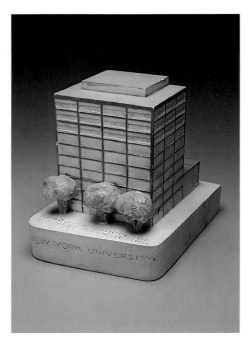

SML 270 NYU Graduate School   1956 C 1956 700
          of Business Administration
          Building

In 1956, the New York advertising agency handling the Johnson & Johnson account was also involved in a fund-raising campaign for a new Graduate Business Administration School building for New York University. The fund-raiser awarded a figurine of the new building to anyone contributing at least $10,000 to the fund. Baston produced 700 models.

SML 271 The Green Giant   1956 C 1956 1,000

The Green Giant was produced as a promotional piece for the Minneapolis food producer. Baston portrayed him holding a yellow ear of corn and a pod of green peas.

SML 272 Michigan Millers Penstand   1956 272 C 1956 1,500
SML 272-A (*Figurine*)   272-A C 1957 1,000

Baston designed an antique mill with an overshot wheel, the Michigan Millers Mutual Life Insurance Company's trademark. First produced as a penstand, the company later used a figurine without the pen.

SML 273 Mayflower (*Painted*) **Penstand**   1957 273 SR 1957–1969
SML 273-A (*Bronzed*) **Penstand**   273-A SR 1957–1969
SML 273-B Mayflower Figurine (*Painted*)   273-B SR 1957–1969
SML 273-C Mayflower (*Without Clouds*)   273-C SR 1970–1975
                                      LR 1976–Present
                                      (No. 6255)
SML 273-D (*New Jersey Descendants*)   273-D C 1970 300

The Mayflower was the ship that carried the Pilgrims from England to New England in 1620. On December 26, they landed at Plymouth Rock. In 1957, a British group sponsored the voyage of a replica of the original Mayflower from Plymouth, England, to Plymouth, Massachusetts, where the vessel remains on exhibit.

Baston designed a penstand, bronzed and painted, and a painted figurine in conjunction with the 1957 sailing. He kept

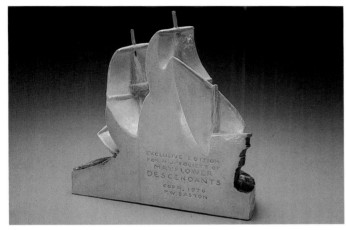

all three designs in his retail line until 1970, when he received an order from the New Jersey Descendants of the Mayflower for 300 pieces. He inscribed their names in the back and, most significantly, removed the cloud background. The painted miniature with the clouds removed has remained in the retail line.

SML 274 Jamestown Church   **SR 1957-1975**

In 1957, Baston, Marjorie and Woody traveled to Jamestown, Virginia, site of the first permanent English settlement in America (est. May 14, 1607) and the capital of Virginia throughout the 17th century. Of the old settlement, only the old

church tower (built c.1639) and a few gravestones were visible when the National Park Service excavations began in 1934.

A tercentenary celebration was held in 1907 and in 1957 the Jamestown Festival Park was built to commemorate the 350th anniversary. The park contains exhibit pavilions and replicas of the first fort and the three ships that brought the first settlers.

While at the park, Baston sold the park gift shop the idea for a series of four pieces; the Church, the Fort, the three ships and a Jamestown glassblower, featured in one of the exhibits. Except for the glassblower (SML 277), the series sold slowly and the three other miniatures are rare.

SML 275 Olde James Fort   **1957 SR 1957-1975**

Designed as one of a group for the Jamestown anniversary (see SML 274), the flat replica of the James Fort was a slow seller and is rare.

SML 276 Jamestown Ships   **1957 SR 1957-1975**

Designed as one of a group for the Jamestown anniversary (see SML 274), the ship plaque was sold at the Festival Park gift shop and is rare.

SML 277 Colonial Glassblower   1957 277 SR 1957–1975
                                                          LR 1976–Present
                                                          (No. 6216)
SML 277-A American Glass Industry   277-A C 1958 1,200
           (Penstand)

Designed as one of a group for the Jamestown anniversary (see SML 274), the miniature was sold throughout Baston's retail stores and has continued to the present. A year after the introduction, an association promoting the 350th anniversary of the American Glass Industry (1608–1958) commissioned Baston to place the design on a commemorative penstand and produce 1,200 pieces for promotional purposes.

SML 278 Colonial Carriage   1957 SR 1957–1975
                                                          LR 1976–Present
                                                          (No. 6215)

The Williamsburg (Virginia) restoration is situated near historic Jamestown (see SML 274). In 1957, Baston designed a typical colonial Williamsburg carriage for sale in their gift shop. The miniature was immediately popular and placed throughout Baston's retail stores.

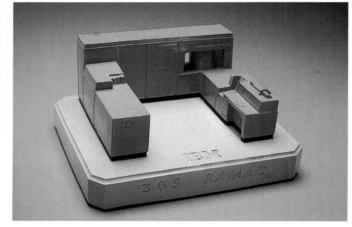

SML 279 IBM 305 Ramac   1957 C 1957 2,000

IBM (then known more widely as International Business Machine), had designed a new large computer system. To launch its introduction, they ordered 2,000 pieces of a miniature version of the complete system and used them for advertising purposes. Baston recalls that in those days only the government and very large companies used computers.

SML 280 Colonial Fund Doorway   1957 C 1957 800

The Colonial Fund in Boston asked Baston to create a penstand they could use for promotional purposes. Using the 1953 Diedrich Knickerbocker figure (SML 145) as his basis, he designed the company's elaborate front door as a plaque background. The "town crier" invites the client to enter. (The photograph shown is missing the penstand.)

SML 281 Speedy Alka Seltzer   1957 C 1957 24

Miles Laboratories asked Baston to design a few dozen miniatures of their trademark, Speedy Alka Seltzer, holding a packaged bottle of Alka Seltzer tablets. After studying the prototypes, the company decided to launch a massive promotional campaign.

When the company asked for delivery dates for 250,000(!) pieces, Baston quietly thanked them for the opportunity to participate and withdrew from the project. "You can imagine what could have happened. The Studio would have folded in favor of the Marblehead Division of Miles Laboratories. My 'no' decision was easier than you might imagine."

SML 282 Nabisco Spoonmen   1957 C 1957 300

The National Biscuit Company, with offices in New York City, asked Baston to design a miniature using spacemen to advertise the company's Shredded Wheat Juniors breakfast cereal. Baston responded with 300 pieces of three little space creatures riding breakfast spoons down a slide. (The third creature in the photo is missing his antenna.)

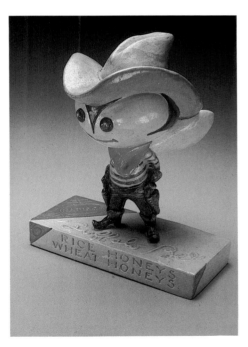

SML 283 Nabisco Buffalo Bee   1957 C 1957 1,500

In 1957, Nabisco was sponsoring a Buffalo Bill children's television program and advertising the company's Rice Honeys and Wheat Honeys brand names. Baston produced 1,500 bees dressed in Buffalo Bill garb that were used by Nabisco to call retailers' attention to the show.

SML 284 Borden's Centennial (*Elsie the Cow*)   1957 C 1957 500

1957 was the 100th anniversary of the Borden Company's founding. Baston designed and produced 500 Elsie the Cows on a pedestal marking the dates 1857–1957.

**SML 285 Williamsburg Couple   1958 SR 1958–1975
LR 1976–Present
(No. 6322)**

In 1958, Baston proposed a project to the Essex County National Bank in Peabody, Massachusetts (now the Essex Bank). The idea was for a penstand with an oval recess into which a series of seven miniatures of various couples could be exchanged. Baston changed his 1947 Pilgrims (SML 72) to a more ornate base and retitled it Thanksgiving Couple. He transferred his R. H. Stearns (Godey) couple (SML 89) to the ornate Victorian Couple base. He presented these two, along with five new joined pairs, to the bank. When the bank decided against

the promotion, all the pairs were placed in the retail line and have been steady sellers since then.

With the Williamsburg Couple, Baston combined his 1939 Williamsburg Governor and Lady pair (SML 7 and 8).

In later years, Baston issued Home from the Sea (SML 365), Sam and Margaret Houston (SML 382), Buffalo Bill and Annie Oakley (SML 384) and Coronado and Senora (SML 383).

**SML 286 John and Priscilla Alden   1958 SR 1955–1975
LR 1976–Present
(No. 6323)**

One of a seven-miniature series of famous couples (see SML 285), Baston combined 1939's John Alden and Priscilla (SML 5 and 6) on one base. He modified the original John Alden so that his head bent down to meet Priscilla.

**SML 287 George and Martha Washington   1958 SR 1958–1975
LR 1976–Present
(No. 6321)**

One of a seven-miniature series of couples (see SML 285), George and Martha are a combination of 1939's original individual designs (SML 3 and 4).

SML 288 Pioneer Couple   1958 SR 1958–1975
                                               LR 1976–Present
                                               (No. 6326)

One of a seven-miniature series of couples (see SML 285), the Pioneer Couple was created by combining 1950's Audrey (SML 158) from Baston's Shakespearean series and the 1955 Davy Crockett (SML 249).

SML 289 Romeo and Juliet   1958 SR 1958–1975

The seventh and final pair of a series of popular couples (see SML 285). The pair was the combination of Baston's 1947 Shakespearean couple (SML 77 and 78) mounted on an ornate base. This couple alone was not continued by Lance and is by far the rarest design in the series.

SML 290 Mt. Vernon   1958 SR 1958–1975

Baston designed Mt. Vernon as a companion miniature to his George and Martha Washington (SML 287). A scale model of Washington's historic Virginia home (complete with pillars for the front porch!), it was sold at the Mt. Vernon gift shop. The piece was very difficult to produce and is rare.

SML 291 Lincoln Memorial (*White*)   1958 291 SR 1958–1975
                                               LR 1976–Present
                                               (No. 6007)
SML 291-A (*Pearl*)   291-A C 1962 2,000
SML 291-B (*White Penstand*)   291-B SR 1958–1967
SML 291-C (*Bronzed*)   291-C SR 1958–1975
SML 291-D (*Bronzed Penstand*)   291-D SR 1958–1967
SML 291-E (*Bronzed Pen and Pencil Set*)   291-E SR 1958

Baston designed his Seated Lincoln as a scale replica of Daniel Chester French's great marble sculpture in Washington, D.C. He produced both figurines and penstands, both in white and bronzed versions. The original white color of French's work was always the most popular and the bronzed versions are much rarer than the white. He also produced a few combination bronzed pen and pencil sets (with the sculpture in the center) and the author has seen one in a private collection.

In 1962, Baston cast 2,000 in a pearly-white substance for the National Secretaries Association. The color difference is obvious when compared with the white but not easy to define when alone.

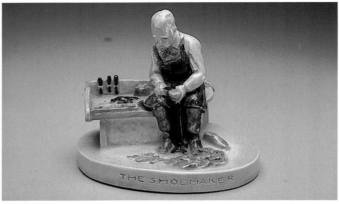

SML 293 Hannah Duston (*Haverhill National*   1958 C 1958 3,000
        Bank Penstand)

Hannah Duston (1657–1729) was captured in a 1697 Indian raid on Haverhill, Massachusetts, and taken up the Merrimack River to a place near modern Concord, N.H. While the Indians were asleep, Hannah and a 10-year-old boy (Samuel Lennardson) killed and scalped ten of their guards and with another prisoner returned to Haverhill.

Baston portrayed her wielding her ax in a penstand design used to promote the 300th anniversary of her birth by the Haverhill National Bank.

SML 292 Shoemaker (*Nat'l Bank of Plymouth, Plymouth County*)	1958 292 C 1958 400
SML 292-A (*National Bank of Plymouth, Brockton*)	292-A C 1958 250
SML 292-B (*Paperweight*)	292-B SR 1959-1962
SML 292-C (*Haverhill Penstand*)	292-C C 1960 1,000
SML 292-D (*Plain Figurine Base*)	292-D SR 1962-1975 LR 1976-Present (No. 6217)
SML 292-E (*First County National Bank*)	292-E C 1962 250
SML 292-F (*International Shoe—Rand Penstand*)	292-F C 1963 100
SML 292-G (*International Shoe—Ewing Penstand*)	292-G C 1963 100

The American shoe industry began in New England and remained a major industry through the 1960's. The Plymouth County National Bank commissioned a Shoemaker design for a commemorative promotion in 1958. After that, Baston received six more commercial orders through 1963 from banks and the International Shoe Company in St. Louis, Missouri. The largest order was for 1,000 penstands inscribed Haverhill National Bank. Rand and Ewing were company executives. In 1959, Baston placed a paperweight version in his retail line and changed that to a plain figurine base in 1962.

SML 294 Salem Savings Bank   1958 294 C 1958 1,200
SML 294-A (*Penstand*)   294-A C 1958 100

1958 marked the 140th anniversary of the founding of the Salem Savings Bank in nearby Salem, Massachusetts. Baston produced 1,200 figurines depicting a relief model of the building's facade. He produced 100 penstand versions for preferred customers. The basic color of both versions was pink (the penstand version, without the pen base, is illustrated).

SML 295 CBS Miss Columbia Penstand	1958 295 C 1958 24
SML 295-A Connecticut Bank and Trust	295-A C 1960 1,000
(*Painted*)	
SML 295-B (*Bronzed*)	295-B C 1961 1,000

The New York agency handling the Columbia Broadcasting System television advertising invited Baston to submit two designs for possible promotional use by CBS. He responded with Jackie Gleason (SML 296) and the general figure of Miss Columbia. He inscribed her flowing shawl with the words "Columbia Broadcasting System, Inc.; Religion, Culture, Education, News, Sports, Adventure." CBS did nothing with the two dozen prototypes.

In 1960 he converted the design to portray cash flow and produced 1,000 pieces for the Connecticut Bank and Trust Co. A year later he produced a bronzed version for the same company.

SML 296 Jackie Gleason   1958 C 1958 6

As part of his CBS proposal (see SML 295), Baston sculpted comedian Jackie Gleason's head on 1951 Francis Drake's (SML 177) upper torso. The old Gleason show (The Honeymooners) had run down in 1957 and there was no Gleason show in 1958. CBS was planning a new Gleason series with sidekick Buddy Hackett, and they were planning a national promotion to introduce "The Great One." Neither the promotion nor the show took hold (it was canceled after a half-season) and Baston was left with a model of Jackie Gleason's head perched on Sir Francis Drake's body to promote an unpromotable show.

SML 297 Harvard Trust Co. Colonial Man	1958 297 C 1958 700
SML 297-A Colonial Watchman	297-A SR 1967–1975
	LR 1976–Present
	(No. 6208)

The Harvard Trust Company commissioned Baston to design a caricature of their company logotype holding a copy of their corporate seal. In 1967, Baston modified his staff-bearing right hand, replaced his seal with a lamp, changed his colors and issued him as Colonial Watchman through his retail stores. He's been a popular seller since.

SML 298 Jordan Marsh Observer   1958 298 C 1958 2,500
    (*Northshore Shopping Center*)
SML 298-A (*A Better Selling Contest Winner*)   298-A C 1958 100
SML 298-B Colonial Overseer   298-B SR 1972–1975
                    LR 1976–Present
                    (No. 6259)

Baston had already designed the Jordan Marsh Company Observer leaning over a construction fence in 1948 (SML 113), escorting Dame New England (SML 189) and riding an "Allied White Horse" (SML 190) in 1951. When Jordan Marsh opened their new store at the Northshore Shopping Center (near Salem), Baston took the original design and replaced the construction fence with lobster traps, buoys and a ship's wheel. The 2,500-piece version was inscribed "Northshore Shopping Center" and was used for a wide handout promotion. Another 100 were inscribed "A Better Selling Contest Winner" and were used in a store sales contest. They are rare.

In 1972, Baston changed the base to "Colonial Overseer" and put it through his retail stores.

SML 299 Cliquot Club Eskimo (*Penstand*)   1958 299 C 1958 2,500
SML 299-A Eskimo   299-A SR 1964–1975

The Cliquot Club Bottling Company ordered 2,500 miniatures of its company logotype Eskimo holding a bottle of Ginger Ale standing on a snow-covered penstand. The company printed 2,500 microminiature labels which were glued on to each bottle.

In 1964, Baston exchanged the bottle with a fish and removed the penstand for a figurine which was first sold at the Alaska display in New York's 1964 World Fair and then distributed through the retail line.

SML 301 Siesta Coffee Penstand   1959 C 1959 1,000

Baston received a commission in 1959 to sculpt a miniature Standard Brands "Siesta Coffee" penstand for use in a *Reader's Digest* advertising promotion. A reprint of the ad was sent with the penstand and the cover of the reprint states: "Muchos Pesos with Siesta."

SML 300 Commodore Stephen Decatur	1958 300 C 1958 1,200
(*Decatur Bank, Bronzed*)	
SML 300-A (*Painted, Museum of the City of New York*)	300-A C 1960 1,000
SML 300-B (*Burrows Gallerye*)	300-B C 1982-Present

Stephen Decatur (1779–1829) joined the U.S. Navy in 1798. During the War of 1812, he gained fame by capturing several British ships with daring tactics. The town of Decatur, Illinois was named after the war hero.

In 1958, Baston was requested by the president of the Decatur National Bank to design and produce 1,200 bronzed Stephen Decaturs for a bank promotion. The man was astonished to hear that Stephen Decatur, a direct descendant of the Commodore, was Baston's next-door neighbor in Marblehead.

In 1960, Baston converted the design to a hexagonal base and inscribed "Museum of the City of New York" for the Museum series (see SML 310) and produced 1,000 pieces. The design was reissued in 1982 as part of the series commissioned by the Museum and Burrows Gallerye in Englewood, New Jersey.

SML 302 Harvard Trust Co. Town Crier	1959 302 C 1959 400
SML 302-A Colonial Bell Ringer	302-A SR 1967-1975
	LR 1976-Present
	(No. 6207)

Following the Harvard Trust Company's Colonial Man (SML 297) the previous year, Baston designed another jovial Colonial character with a bell in one hand and cane in the other. Inscribed "Harvard Trust Co.," only 400 pieces were produced. In 1967, Baston changed the inscription of Colonial Bell Ringer and reintroduced him (with Colonial Watchman, SML 297-A) in the retail line.

SML 303 Mrs. S.O.S. 1959 C 1959 3,000

Baston designed a caricature of Mrs. S.O.S. from the *New Yorker* cartoons by Hoff. The figurines, like Siesta Coffee (SML 301), were purchased by *Reader's Digest* for S.O.S. salesmen to hand-out to their customers. The miniatures were included in a *Reader's Digest* merchandising package.

The hang-tag accompanying the figurine reads as follows: "Meet Mrs. S.O.S. She'll help you clean up! A lady with an eye toward making sales for you. Through regular advertising in *Reader's Digest*, S.O.S. Scouring Pad messages reach at least every fourth home in your community. They are read by your customers who have faith and confidence in *Reader's Digest* and who rely on products advertised in its pages.

"Keep Mrs. S.O.S. on your desk. Let her be your reminder to keep plenty of S.O.S. Magic Scouring Pads in stock."

SML 304 H. P. Hood Co. 1959 C 1959 200
Cigar Store Indian

H. P. Hood, the Boston dairy, produced an orange drink with the brandname "Southern Sun." In 1959, the company ordered 200 replicas of the Seminole cigar store Indian used as the orange juice trademark.

Baston says the miniature is "An awful replica of an Indian but an exact replica of Hood's trademark."

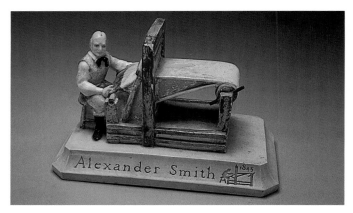

SML 305 Alexander Smith Weaver 1959 C 1959 1,000

The Alexander Smith Carpet Co., with main offices in New York City, used a man weaving at a hand loom as their logotype. Based on a contract order for 1,000 Sebastians for use in a promotion, Baston traveled to one of their mills in upper New York state for research on one of Smith's antique looms. The miniature replica is authentic.

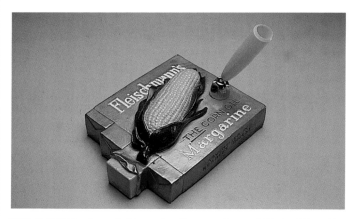

SML 306 Fleischman's Margarine Penstand 1959 C 1959 1,500

In a *Reader's Digest* merchandise rebate similar to Siesta Coffee and Mrs. S.O.S. (SML 301 and 303), Baston produced 1,500 penstands advertising Fleischman's Margarine ("Advertised in *Reader's Digest*"). Four quarter-pound foil wrappers support an ear of corn. The margarine extends from the third quarter.

SML 307 Fleischman's Margarine Penstand 1959 C 1959 1,000

One Fleischman penstand was designed as a salesman's handout (SML 306). Another was designed for mailing. Using only two quarter-pounds, with the margarine exposed on the second quarter, this design required less expensive packaging and postage.

SML 308 Alcoa Wrap Penstand   1959 C 1959 1,500

Designed as another *Reader's Digest* merchandise rebate, the penstand places the Aluminum Company of America's double triangle trademark, designed into a strong man, on a large and smaller box of "Super Strength" Alcoa Wrap. A piece of metal is cast into the figure to support the thin junction point of the triangles.

SML 309 Stagecoach Penstand   1959 309 C 1959 500
     (*Everett National Bank*)
SML 309-A Stagecoach   309-A SR 1960–1975
                                    LR 1976–Present
                                      (No. 6258)

Baston designed a stagecoach penstand for the Everett National Bank, Everett, Mass. to hand out to their customers. The stagecoach was the bank's trademark because Everett was the Boston terminal of the Newburyport (on the Massachusetts north shore) Turnpike. Most of the stage lines traveled this route.

Jeremiah Prescott, Baston's great grandfather, drove this stagecoach line during the 1830's.

A year later, Baston removed the penstand and changed the base to the simple "Stagecoach." It has sold in the retail line since that time.

SML 310 Fiorello LaGuardia   1959 310 C 1959 1,000
SML 310-A (*Burrows Gallerye*)   310-A C 1982–Present

Fiorello H. LaGuardia (1882–1947) served as Mayor of New York City from 1934 to 1945. He executed a vast program of reform, reduced political corruption, forwarded the modernizing of New York City, brought about the adoption (1938) of a new city charter, introduced slum clearance projects and improved health and sanitary conditions. "The Little Flower" (from his Italian name) was re-elected Mayor for three consecutive terms but chose not to run in 1945. His life was the subject of 1960's Broadway hit musical "Fiorello!"

The Museum of the City of New York (formerly the Mayor's mansion) asked Baston to create a series of famous New Yorkers for sale in the Museum's gift shop, beginning with LaGuardia. He designed a six-sided base for the caricature of the Italian-American and then went on to create a serious historic series including Hudson, Verrazano, Stuyvesant and Decatur.

In 1982, as part of the reissued Museum series, LaGuardia was brought out 100 years after his birth. The Museum and Burrows Gallerye are inscribed in the base.

117

SML 311 Henry Hudson   1959 311 1959 1,000
SML 311-A (*Burrows Gallerye*)   311-A C 1981-Present

Henry Hudson, English navigator and explorer, sailed in the *Half Moon* to Chesapeake Bay, Delaware Bay and New York Bay. He was the first white man to sail the Hudson River (1607) nearly up to present-day Albany. His voyage gave the Dutch their claim to that region.

Baston sculpted the sailor as part of his Museum of the City of New York series (see SML 310). The miniature was reissued in 1981 as a commission of Burrows Gallerye and the Museum.

SML 312 Giovanni Verrazano   1959 312 C 1959 1,000
SML 312-A (*Burrows Gallerye*)   312-A C 1982-Present

Giovanni Verrazano (1480–1527) Italian navigator, was possibly the first European to enter New York Bay. In 1524, Verrazano explored the North American coast, probably from North Carolina to Maine. Based on his discoveries, his brother Gerolamo's maps (1529) showed a new concept of North America. The Verrazano-Narrows Bridge (1964) spanning the entry to New York harbor bears his name.

Baston sculpted him as part of the Museum of the City of New York series (see SML 310). The miniature was reissued in 1982 as a commission of Burrows Gallerye and the Museum.

SML 313 Peter Stuyvesant   1960 313 C 1960 1,000
SML 313-A (*Burrows Gallerye*)   313-A C 1981-Present

Peter Stuyvesant (1610–1672) was Dutch director general of New Amsterdam (later New York City) beginning in 1647. Overwhelmed by a surprise attack, Stuyvesant surrendered New Amsterdam in 1664. He spent the rest of his life on his Manhattan farm and was buried there under his chapel, now the site of a church, St. Mark's-in-the-Bowery.

This design for the Museum of the City of New York (see SML 310), had nothing to do with his 1949 portrayal (SML 23). The miniature was reissued in 1981 as a commission of Burrows Gallerye and the Museum.

SML 314 Masonic Bible   1960 C 1960 250

Marblehead Masons celebrated their 200th anniversary on March 25, 1960. Baston designed a Bible, compass and square with the following inscription cast into the rear of the base:

"This square and compass represents the set used by philanthropic lodge A.F. & A.M. [Ancient Fraternal and Accepted Masons]. The originals were captured from the British ship *Hope* in 1776 by the privateer *Franklin* commanded by Captain James Mugford of Marblehead."

118

SML 315 Mark Twain　　　　　　1960 SR 1960-1975
　　　　　　　　　　　　　　　　　　LR 1976-Present
　　　　　　　　　　　　　　　　　　　　(No. 6137)

Mark Twain, the pseudonym of Samuel Langhorne Clemens (1835–1910), was an American author, humorist, narrator and social observer. Twain wrote *Tom Sawyer* in 1876 while living in Hartford, Connecticut, and *The Adventures of Huckleberry Finn* in 1884. The latter, his masterpiece, is called the first American novel by many.

Baston added the miniature, taken from a series of photographs on the veranda of a friend's home in Peterborough, New Hampshire, to his 1948 series of Twain's fictional characters (SML 94–99).

SML 316 Gem Crib & Cradle Co.　　1960 316 C 1960 500
　　　　Gibson Girl
SML 316-A Gibson Girl　　　　　　316-A SR 1962-1975
　　　　　　　　　　　　　　　　　　LR 1976-Present

Baston designed a Gibson Girl with her baby for the Gem Crib and Cradle Co. Charles Dana Gibson (1867–1944), the American illustrator, modeled his drawings on his wife, the fashionable Irene Langhorne. Women during the gay '90's imitated her clothes, looks and manners.

Baston submitted an ashtray design prototype (illustrated) but Gem decided on a simpler and less expensive figurine. Two years later, Baston changed the base to Gibson Girl at Home and placed it in his retail line with his 1951 series of three (SML 172–174).

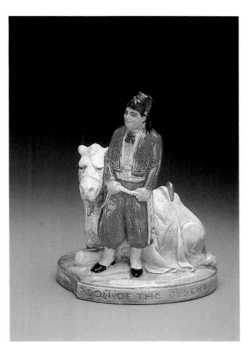

SML 317 Son of the Desert　　　1960 317 SR 1960-1962
SML 317-A (*Allepo*)　　　　　　317-A C 1961 100
SML 317-B (*Medina*)　　　　　　317-B C 1962 200
SML 317-C The Shriner　　　　　317-C SR 1962-1975

Many Baston dealers and collectors had requested a Shriner over the years. In 1960, Baston designed Son of the Desert. The Allepo Temple of Shriners in Boston ordered 100 pieces with their name added to the base and the Medina Temple in Chicago asked for 200 a year later. In 1962, he changed the name of his original retail piece to "The Shriner."

SML 318 Metropolitan Life Tower Penstand   1960 C 1960 1,200

Another *Reader's Digest* merchandise rebate (see SML 303), Baston produced 1,200 replicas of the Metropolitan Life Insurance Company tower on a penstand base. The company's agents received the miniature as a reminder that the home office was generating advertising leads for them.

SML 319 The Grocery Store (*Initials***)**   1960 319 C 1960–1961 500
SML 319-A The Grocery Store   319-A SR 1962–1975
     LR 1976–Present

Baston designed a grocery store owner for an independent food jobber in Rye, New York. During 1960 and 1961, Baston offered to inscribe the initials of a store owner in the base, 15 cents an initial with a maximum of three initials. A jobber salesman would request the specific initials, Baston would scribe them in, send the miniature to the salesman and he would present it to his customer.

In 1962, Baston converted the base to the Grocery Store and added it to his retail line.

SML 320 Supp-hose Lady   1960 320 C 1960 1,500
SML 320-A (*Penstand***)**   320-A C 1961 500

The last of Baston's *Reader's Digest* rebate programs, the Supp-Hose lady demonstrates "Gently Supported" legs. A year later, *Reader's Digest* ordered 500 penstands.

SML 321 Marine Memorial   1960 C 1960–1961 1,000

A marble sculpture stands as a memorial to seamen in Hampton Beach, New Hampshire. The State of New Hampshire Tourist Division ordered 1,000 marbleized miniature replicas of the original to promote tourist attention. The inscription on the base reads: "Breathe Soft, Ye Winds, Ye Waves, In Silence Rest."

SML 322 The Infantryman   1960 C 1960 700

A Marblehead acquaintance had ties with the Infantry Training Center at Fort Benning, Georgia. In 1960, Marjorie and Woody (then 15) traveled to Georgia and procured photos and books of the heroic statue at the entrance to the famous camp. Baston designed a scale miniature replica and sold it through the PX on the base.

SML 323 Manger   1961 SR 1961–1975
                                                LR 1976–Present
                                                (No. 6315)

Baston needed a lower-priced Nativity grouping than his large 1954 Nativity (SML 233). He broke that piece down into three major elements and sold them as a collectible continuity series. The standard for current miniaturization is 1:12 scale, or one inch for every foot. With this series, Baston had worked in 1:48, or one inch for every four feet.

SML 324 Wisemen   1961 SR 1961–1975
                                                LR 1976–Present
                                                (No. 6316)

This scene is the second of the Nativity series (SML 323).

SML 325 Shepherds   1961 SR 1961–1975
                                                LR 1976–Present
                                                (No. 6317)

The third of the Nativity series (SML 323).

SML 326 Ben Franklin at The Printing Press 1961 326 C 1961 500
   (*Curtis Publishing*)
SML 326-A (*Plain*)   326-A SR 1962–1975
                                                LR 1976–Present
                                                (No. 6218)

The Curtis Publishing Company (*Saturday Evening Post*) ordered 500 miniatures depicting Ben Franklin at an 18th century printing press. Curtis used it in a promotion in 1961. The base is inscribed "Curtis Publishing Co."

A year later, Baston removed the "Curtis" and placed the miniature in his retail line.

SML 327 Tony Piet   1961 327 C 1961 200
SML 327-A (*Bookend*)   327-A C 1961 10
SML 328 Bunky Knudsen   328 C 1961 200
SML 328-A (*Bookend*)   328-A C 1961 10
SML 328-B (*Together on Penstand*)   328-B C 1961 50

Tony Piet (Anthony Pietruszka) was a second baseman for the Chicago White Sox from 1935 to 1937. Bunky Knudsen was an executive for the Pontiac Car Division of General Motors. In 1961, they planned a special promotion for Piet's Chicago Pontiac dealership. Baston designed and cast 200 figurines of each, ten sets of Piet-Knudsen bookends and 50 pen and pencil stands with a man on each side and a Pontiac in the middle. All versions were sprayed with gold paint.

SML 329 Merchant's Warren Sea Captain   1961 C 1961 1,000

The Merchants Warren National Bank in Salem commissioned Baston to design and produce a miniature commemorating the bank's 150th anniversary (1811–1961). Baston knew from research that wealthy sea merchants were typical Atlantic seacoast financial institution entrepreneurs during that time. He modeled the captain's hat from a collection in the Peabody Institute in Salem.

SML 330 Savin' Sandy (*McNeill*)   1961 330 C 1961 300
SML 330-A (*Brown's*)   330-A C 1962 600
SML 330-B (*Plain*)   330-B SR 1962–1975
SML 330-C (*Armstrong*)   330-C C 1981–1982 11,000
SML 330-D (*Plain*)   330-D LR 1982–Present
                                (No. 2470)

Baston designed a Scotsman with a green and yellow McNeill tartan for McNeill Laboratories. One of their medicines was being promoted as less expensive than other brands. A year later, Baston produced 600 for Brown's department store in Gloucester, Massachusetts. He used the McMillan tartan of yellow and brown. The same year he put Sandy in the retail line without the Brown's inscription.

In 1981, he painted the tartan the Armstrong green with red tam as a commission for Armstrong's, a dealer in Pomona, California, and produced 11,000 pieces. In 1982 the "Armstrong's" was removed from the base and put back in the retail line.

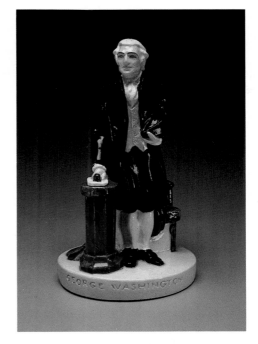

SML 331 George Washington, Mason   1961 331 SR 1961–1975
                                                       LR 1976–Present
                                                       (No. 6005)

SML 331-A (*Penstand*)   331-A SR 1961–1967
SML 331-B (*A.F. & A.M.; without chair*)   331-B C 1963 1,500
SML 331-C (*With Magnets*)   331-C C 1964 1,000
SML 331-D (*Without Sash*)   331-D LR 1982–Present
                                                       (No. 2448)

George Washington was the only president to be master of a Mason's lodge and President of the United States at the same time. At the request of several collectors, Baston designed the first president in his Masonic regalia, both as a figurine and penstand, for the retail line.

In 1963, he cast 1,500 for the A.F. & A.M. in Marblehead, this time without a chair to keep production time and expenses down. Then, in response to another request, Baston cast 1,000 pieces with magnets in the base. Some Masons wanted to place the figurine on their car dashboard.

Sebastian discontinued the George Washington with cannon figurine in 1980 (SML 84). To get a more conservative Washington in the line, Baston removed the Masonic garb in 1982.

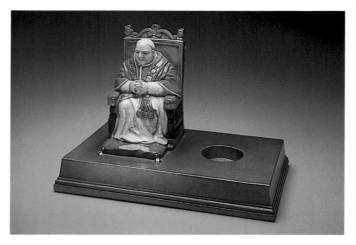

| SML 332 Pope John 23rd | 1961 332 C 1961 1,500 |
| SML 332-A (*Penstand*) | 332-A C 1961 500 |

Theron Pritchard, the Chicago detective who began soliciting Sebastian business (see page 25), secured a contract from the Chicago archdiocese Roman Catholic newspaper. The order was for 1,500 figurines and 500 penstands depicting Pope John the 23rd, pope from 1958 to 1963. The Kane family of Swampscott personally presented one of the figurines to Pope John during a formal audience at the Vatican in 1962.

| SML 334 Seamen's Bank for Savings | 1962 324 C 1962 1,000 |
| SML 334-A (*Barometer*) | 334-A C 1962 100 |

The Seamen's Bank for Savings in Salem commissioned Baston to design a miniature replica of their bank seal. The Indian on the left has brought his furs to market and the seaman on the right uses the bank to secure his funds, while an eagle connects the two. 1,000 bronzed pieces were used by the bank.

Baston cast an additional 100 pieces with a small barometer placed in the back. The bank distributed these to preferred customers.

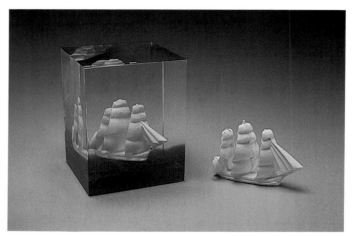

| SML 335 Yankee Clipper Sulfide | 1962 C 1962 1,500 |

The New England Mutual Insurance Company ordered 1,500 small white Yankee Clippers encased in a cube of lucite for promotional purposes. Baston designed a micro-miniature sailing ship (3 masts and 14 sails in a model less than an inch long), cast 1,500 sulfides (a small white design usually encased in glass) and had them cast into a lucite cube. A blue base in the plastic represents the sea.

Francis Hatch, the New England Mutual project supervisor, was unsuccessful candidate for Republican governor of Massachusetts in 1978.

| SML 333 St. Jude Thaddeus | 1961 C 1961 1,000 |

St. Jude, one of the Twelve Disciples, is thought to have been the brother of St. James the Less. According to Western tradition he suffered martyrdom in Persia with St. Simon, with whom he shares a feast (October 28).

Baston produced this design for St. Jude's Church in Chicago. The statue portrays Jude holding a small bust of Jesus.

SML 336 Big Brother Bob Emery   1962 C 1962 25

This miniature represents the pinnacle of Baston's commercial ingenuity. Bob Emery was a popular radio entertainer on Boston station WBZ. The afternoon before, Baston received a frantic call from the station to ask if he could cast up two dozen figurines appropriate for the next day's 65th birthday party for Emery.

That afternoon, Baston used the Alexander Smith Weaver base (SML 305), modified the head and arms of Mark Twain (SML 315) and lopped off the front two rows of Swan Boat (SML 150). The next morning, one of his workers cast 25 pieces, cleaned and painted them and two dozen were delivered to the station for the evening party. Big Brother Bob Emery received a figurine of himself relaxing with his ukelele while a group of youngsters listen.

SML 337 Blue Belle Highlander	1962 337 C 1962 300
SML 337-A The Piper	337-A SR 1962–1975
SML 337-B (*Armstrong's*)	337-B C 1982–Present

The Masons in Lynn, Massachusetts sponsored a girl's bagpipe band that played at Masonic parades and functions. The group wanted 300 "Blue Belle Highlanders" for use in raising funds for costumes and trips. Baston portrayed her with a red tartan with black stripes and red bagpipe cords. That same year he converted her to "The Piper," with a yellow tartan with red stripes and yellow cords. When Armstrong's in Pomona, California, commissioned an Armstrong Piper in 1982, Baston changed her tam to red, her tartan to green with red stripes and her pipe cords to green.

SML 338 John F. Kennedy
1963 SR 1963–1975
LR 1976–Present
(No. 6008)

Massachusetts Senator John F. Kennedy was elected President of the United States in November, 1960. Baston added him to his series of U.S. presidents in the beginning of 1963 and the miniature has remained in the retail line.

SML 339 John F. Kennedy Toby Jug   1963 332 C 1963 25
SML 340 Jackie Kennedy Toby Jug   333 C 1963 25

A toby jug is a small pottery pitcher modeled in the form of a person's head, a corner of which serves as a pourer. The jug is also called a fillpot, both names taken from Toby Filpot, inebriate character in the 18th century British song "Little Brown Jug."

Baston designed two-dozen prototypes of Jack and Jackie to be transferred into 50,000 sets of porcelain jiggers in Japan for distribution by Schmid. The young president was assassinated on November 22 by Lee Harvey Oswald and, of course, the project was cancelled.

SML 341 Naumkeag Indian   1963 334 C 1963 1,000
SML 341-A (Bronzed)   334-A C 1964 500

Baston banked at the Naumkeag Trust Company in Salem, a competitor of the Merchants Warren. In 1963 he showed his bank the competition figure (SML 331) and the president ordered 1,000 painted trademarks of *his* bank. A year later they ordered 500 bronzed versions.

SML 342 Dia-Mel Fat Man   1963 C 1963 800

Someone at the Dia-Mel Company, manufacturers of diet food supplements, saw the old (1952) Jell-O Fat Man (SML 201) and requested a similar design. Baston used the scale and modified the man (bald vs. hair and hands folded vs. hanging down). The base advises that you "Balance the Scales."

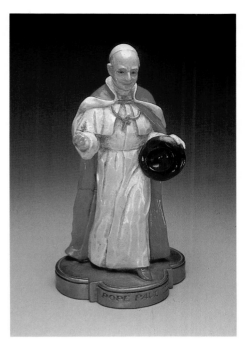

SML 343 Pope Paul VI   1965 SR 1965–1975

Pope Paul VI visited the United States in 1965. He spoke to the United Nations, conducted a gigantic open air mass in Yankee Stadium and, as the first pope to ever visit the United States, captured the attention of all Americans. Baston sculpted him as an active traveler and enjoyed great success with the figurine for the next year-and-a-half through his retail and religious stores.

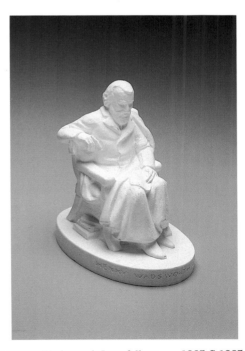

SML 344 Henry Wadsworth Longfellow   1965 C 1965–1967 300

A good Sebastian dealer in Portland, Maine requested a miniature replica of the Longfellow bronze in that city. Baston made this miniature especially for him, bronzed it, and sold him a few hundred over a three-year period.

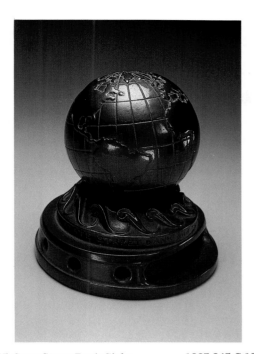

SML 345 State Street Bank Globe   1965 345 C 1965 1,200
SML 345-A (*Thermometer*)   345-A C 1965 400

The State Street Bank & Trust Company in Boston asked Baston to design a globe for them to be used for promotional purposes. He executed a sharp and accurate globe and produced 1,200 on solid bases and 400 on latticed bases containing horizontal Fahrenheit/Celsius thermometers (illustrated). The globe was later used in Uncle Sam in Orbit (SML 364).

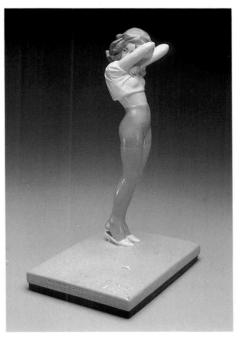

SML 346 Panti-Legs Girl (*Penstand*)   1965 C 1965 400

In a wide diversion from his traditional work, Baston designed this shapely woman to advertise the new panty hose just beginning to appear on the market. The girl is a sculptural version of a decorative design printed on the Glen Raven Company's packing box. The penstand was used for promotion.

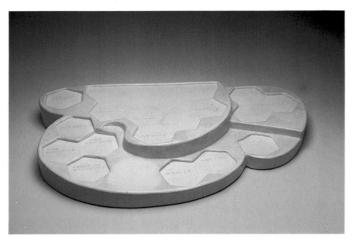

SML 347 Dickens Collection Base 1966 SR 1966-1975
LR 1976-Present
(No. 6118)

Baston had sold his Dickens series continuously since 1946 (see entry prior to SML 49). In 1966, 20 years later, he designed a green Ceramastone base to display the collection. He sold it through his retailers and it is still in the line.

SML 348 Paul Revere Plaque 1966 C 1966 300
(*W.T. Grant*)

The New England regional sales office of the W. T. Grant Company conducted a sales contest for its employees in 1966. Baston used his 1951 Sebastian Plaque bulletin board (SML 168) and his 1950 Paul Revere (SML 152) to create a distinctively New England award "For Outstanding Contribution."

SML 349 New England SPCA 1966 C 1966-1968 2,000

The New England Society for the Prevention of Cruelty to Animals has a marble sculpture located in their Boston headquarters lobby. In 1966, they asked Baston to design a marbleized replica of the sculpture for use in their 1968 centennial celebrating the 100th anniversary of their founding. In 1967 and '68 they used 2,000 miniatures.

SML 350 Little George 1966 C 1966 2,500

The Nashville National Bank in Tennessee had seen some of Baston's miniatures and in 1966 they asked him to design a caricature of George Washington, their logotype. Baston designed "Little George," a style he would later modify for "George and the Hatchet" (SML 367) in his retail line.

SML 354 Town Lyne Indian   1966 C 1966 500

The Town Lyne House restaurant, located north of Boston, ordered 500 pieces of a miniature design of their trademark. The figurines were sold at the restaurant gift shop.

SML 351 Gardeners (*Thermometer*)	1966 343 SR 1966
SML 352 Gardener Man	344 SR 1966-1968
SML 353 Gardener Woman	345 SR 1966-1968

Baston had worked with a thermometer with his State Street Bank Globe (SML 345). Many of his retailers had asked for a "functional" Sebastian over the years. Using the style reminiscent of his 1942 Children's Band (SML 42–47), he designed a gardening couple against a backdrop of a vertical Fahrenheit/-Celsius thermometer. After he had produced about 100 pieces, he started getting complaints on the thermometers "reading all wrong." He realized it was impossible to accurately calibrate a liquid-cast element with a separate glass rod, and he discontinued the model.

He then cast the man and woman as separate figurines, but they lacked the Sebastian look and never sold well in stores. He stopped everything in 1968.

SML 355 Johnny Appleseed	1967 355 C 1967 1,000
(*Apple Industry*)	
SML 355-A (*Non-Commercial*)	355-A SR 1968-1975
	LR 1976-Present
	(No. 6203)

Johnny Appleseed was the nickname of John Chapman (1774–1845), American folk hero. Born in Massachusetts, Chapman wandered westward to Pennsylvania, Ohio, Illinois and Indiana. For 50 years he led a nomadic existence, preaching and distributing apple seeds to all he met. It is said that the orchards of the four states owe their origins to Chapman's seeds.

Baston originally designed his miniature for an industry association that promoted Appleseed as "Patron Saint of the Apple Industry." A year leater he converted the design to a simple "Johnny Appleseed," a retail miniature.

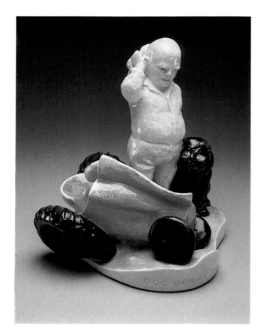

SML 357 Uncle Sam   1967 SR 1967–1975
LR 1976–1981

(Discontinued forever on Oct. 31, 1981)

"Uncle Sam" is a commonly accepted personification of the U.S. government. He may have been inspired by the nickname of a government inspector named Samuel Wilson (1766–1854) of Troy, N.Y. He was an inspector of army supplies and the "U.S." on his stamp was referred to as "Uncle Sam" by his workmen.

Or it may represent an extension of the U.S. initials that sprang up anonymously. At any rate, *The Adventures of Uncle Sam* (1816) by "Frederick Fidfaddy" is the earliest use of the name in a book.

Wilson, a cousin of John Chapman (Johnny Appleseed; SML 356) lived with him at one time in Mason, New Hampshire. Baston first designed the piece for a town celebration and then distributed it through his retail stores. On October 31, 1981, the molds were destroyed forever.

SML 356 Doc Berry of Berwick   1967 356 C 1967 150
SML 356-A (*Lime Shirt*)   356-A C 1979 896
SML 356-B (*Brown Shirt; Boys Camp Fund*)   356-B LR 1981 9,000

Dr. H. Meredith Berry was co-founder of Camp Berwick, a Boys Camp in Maine. In 1967, Baston designed Doc Berry standing next to a dilapidated tractor and his old dog. Baston produced 150 figurines for a fund-raising birthday party.

In 1978, an East Bridgewater, Massachusetts dealer commissioned 10,000 Doc Berrys to raise funds for the camp. Doc Berry had died in July and the dealer's wife was a nurse who had assisted him in operations. After a large promotion with large sales, the dealer encountered financial problems and had to close the issue at 896 pieces. That issue portrayed a lime shirt.

Baston reactivated the promotion in 1981, and the remaining 9,000 were sold as numbered pieces through retail dealers. The last design depicted a brown shirt and tractor and contained the words "Boys Camp Fund" in the base. In 1982, Baston presented the camp board with a check for $22,500 to be used as the board chose, probably for scholarships.

SML 358 Ortho-Novum   1967 C 1967 12

The Ortho Pharmaceutical Company asked Baston to sculpt a three-dimensional version of a *New Yorker* cartoon for use in advertising their Ortho-Novum generic tradename. The cartoon showed a doctor standing in front of his files ordering back a snake who has snuck down from his position on the caduceus (the twin serpents of Hermes). The magazine refused to clear the use of the cartoon and the project died with a dozen samples.

SML 360 Concord Minuteman   1967 SR 1967–1975
                                  LR 1976–Present
                                  (No. 6250

Daniel Chester French's bronze Minuteman is located at Concord Bridge in Concord, Massachusetts. On April 19, 1775, the minuteman of the surrounding areas fired on the British, marking the beginning of the Revolutionary War. French's sculpture has become a symbol of American patriotic spirit.

SML 359 Robert E. Lee   1967 359 SR 1967–1975
    (*At Horse's Head*)   LR 1976–Present
                                  (No. 6009)
SML 359-A (*C.S.A.*)   359-A SR 1968–1969
SML 359-B (*At Horse's Side*) 359-B SR 1968–1975

General Robert E. Lee (1807–1870) accepted command of his native Virginia forces in 1861 at the outset of the Civil War. His defeat at Gettysburg began the attrition of Confederate strength that compelled him to surrender to Grant at Appomattox Court House on April 9, 1865. An excellent stragetist, he is admired in both the North and South for his courage and chivalry.

Baston designed Lee and his horse to join the Famous Americans in the retail line. An Atlanta dealer persuaded him to cast the initials C.S.A. (Confederate States of America) to "increase sales in the South." He sold a few hundred of these. In 1968 he repositioned Lee at the side of his horse, put him on a large base, and sold him as a pair with the white Seated Lincoln Memorial (SML 291). He sold about 1,000.

SML 361 Capt. John Parker   1968 361 SR 1968–1975
SML 361-A (*Lexington Minuteman*)   361-A LR 1976–1977
              (*Discontinued forever on Oct. 31, 1977*)

As the British advance column reached Lexington, Massachusetts (April 19, 1775), they came upon a group of militia (the minutemen). After a brief exchange of shots in which several Americans were killed, the Americans withdrew and the British advanced to Concord. Captain John Parker, the first American to fall in the war, is immortalized in a bronze sculpture on the Lexington Green. The sculpture is more popularly known as the Lexington Minuteman, but Baston kept the original name.

Lance kept the design in the 1976 transition to Hudson but discontinued it forever on Oct. 31, 1977.

131

SML 362 Drummer Boy (*Red*)　　　1968 362 SR 1968–1970
SML 362-A (*Blue*)　　　　　　　362-A SR 1970–1975
　　　　　　　　　　　　　　　LR 1976–Present
　　　　　　　　　　　　　　　　(No. 6209)

The Drummer Boy Gift Shop on Cape Cod asked Baston for a special design. He converted his 1953 Parade Rest Godey Child (SML 216) from Civil War hat to Colonial hat. In 1970 he changed the coat from the British red to the Colonial blue in preparation for the Bicentennial celebration.

SML 363 Water Mill Candy Plaque　　　1968 C 1968 12

The Sturbridge Candy & Gift Shop in Sturbridge, Massachusetts, asked Baston to design a bas relief of a New England water mill. The store used the plaque to shape plastic molds, used in pouring chocolate candy discs. The store still has the molds.

SML 364 Uncle Sam in Orbit　　　1970 SR 1970–1975

Neil Armstrong and Buzz Aldrin had become the first men to walk on the moon in July, 1969. In 1970, Baston designed a miniature to commemorate the event. He used his 1967 Uncle Sam (SML 357) and 1965 Globe (SML 345) and added a moon. The piece sold in his retail stores.

SML 365 Home from the Sea　　　1970 SR 1970–1975
　　　　　　　　　　　　　　　LR 1976–Present
　　　　　　　　　　　　　　　　(No. 6327)

The Famous Couples series (1958, beginning SML 285), lacked a seafaring subject. In 1970, Baston used his 1950 Tom Bowline, Ashore (SML 146) and Phoebe (SML 163) from the House of Seven Gables and mounted them on the ornate couples base.

SML 367 George and the Hatchet   1972 367 SR 1972-1975
SML 368 Martha and the Cherry Pie   368 SR 1972-1975

Designed to sell as a Bicentennial pair, Baston modified his 1966 Little George (SML 350) to hold a hatchet and sculpted a new Martha carrying a cherry pie. The pair was a moderate seller, but Lance did not feel the designs were typical Sebastian and did not continue production.

SML 366 Town Meeting Plaque   1971 366 SR 1971-1975
SML 366-A Sebastian Knickerbocker   366-A 1982-Present
      Plaque   (No. 2274)

Baston designed a New England Town Meeting plaque using the frame of his 1951 Sebastian plaque (SML 168) and 1952 Diedrich Knickerbocker figurine (SML 145). He produced about 100 for use as handouts to promote attendance at meetings. In 1982, he changed the wording on the billboard and the miniature became the new Sebastian display plaque.

SML 369 Sidewalk Days (*Boy*)   1978 LR 1978-1980 10,000
SML 370 Sidewalk Days (*Girl*)   (*Limited Edition of 10,000*
      Issued: July, 1978.
      Fully Subscribed: August, 1980)

Baston designed a boy and his sister on roller skates in 1939. Carbone and he decided the pair did not "fit" with the early historic couples (1938-1939) and Baston never produced the pair. In an historic move, Sebastian Miniatures entered the new (since 1970?) limited edition art market in July, 1978. The Sidewalk Days pair was announced as a limited issue of 10,000 sets at the South Bend (Indiana) Collectors Show. Collector interest started to grow, with a new generation of national dealers and collectors suddenly aware of the forty-year-old name. The issue was fully subscribed in August, 1980.

This pair was the first of Baston's "Children at Play" series.

SML 371 Family Sing   **1978 LR 1978–1979**
(Discontinued forever on December 31, 1979)

Baston planned a new series called "America Remembers" where a Victorian family would participate in significant family activities of turn-of-the-century America. With Family Sing, Baston portrayed the mother at the piano with the father, brother and sister grouped around it in song.

The miniature was introduced at the South Bend Collectors Show in July, 1978 and attracted little interest. In January, 1979, it was announced that the miniature would be discontinued forever on December 31, and brisk sales followed.

SML 372 Mt. Rushmore   **1978 LR 1978–Present**
                                             (No. 6010)

The Mt. Rushmore National Memorial is located in Southwest South Dakota, in the Black Hills. There, carved on the face of a mountain and visible for 60 miles, are the enormous busts of four U.S. Presidents (left to right), Washington, Jefferson, Theodore Roosevelt and Lincoln. The sculpture was nearly completed when the sculptor, Gutzon Borglum, died in 1941. It was finished later that year by his son, Lincoln. In all it took 14 years to complete the figures.

Baston was asked by Kay Riordan, owner of the Mountain Company (Mt. Rushmore gift shop), to sculpt a miniature replica for sale in her shop. He sculpted a large one (page 144) that was judged too large for production and then further scaled down to a miniature that was placed in the retail line.

SML 373 Skipping Rope   **1978 LR 1978–Present**
                                              (No. 6237)

Lance asked Baston to add to his popular 1953 Godey Children (see SML 213) series. With Skipping Rope, he portrayed a young girl in Victorian dress with her jump rope.

SML 374 Little Sister   **1979 LR 1979–Present**
                                              (No. 6238)

The eighth of his Godey Children (see SML 213), Baston portrayed a pair for the first time in the series. The brother, in formal Victorian dress, is tending to his sister.

SML 375 Building Days (*Boy*)   1979 LR 1978–1980 10,000
SML 376 Building Days (*Girl*)   (*Limited Edition of 10,000 sets.*
Issued: January, 1979.
Fully Subscribed: Oct. 1980)

The second limited edition "Children at Play" set (see SML 369), Building Days was introduced at the 1979 Atlantic City China and Glass show. Not heavily subscribed at first, the pair was fully subscribed in October, 1980, two months after the sellout of Sidewalk Days.

Baston portrays a brother and sister playing with their wooden blocks and building toys on a rainy Spring afternoon.

SML 378 Snow Days (*Boy*)   1980 LR Jan. 1980–Nov. 1980 10,000
SML 379 Snow Days (*Girl*)   (*Limited Edition of 10,000 sets.*
Issued: January, 1980.
Fully Subscribed: Nov. 1980)

The third limited "Children at Play" set (see SML 369), Snow Days was introduced at the 1980 Atlantic City China and Glass Show. The pair was fully subscribed in November, 1980, three months after the sellout of Sidewalk Days and one month following Building Days.

Baston portrays the brother and sister engaged in a backyard snowball fight.

SML 377 Rub-a-Dub-Dub   1979 LR 1979-Present
(No. 6404)

Baston had begun design of Rub-a-Dub-Dub, Three Men in a Tub, several years before for an unsuccessful commercial proposal. He finished the work in 1978 and the miniature was released to retail stores in January, 1979. His 1949 set of three nursery rhymes (see SML 137) was originally designed for a music box series, and the scale of Rub is much larger than the original three. This last design never sold as one of the series.

SML 380 Family Picnic   1980 LR 1980
(*Discontinued forever on December 31, 1980*)

The second in the "America Remembers" series (see SML 371), Baston portrayed the Victorian family picnicking on a lazy Sunday afternoon.

This miniature was so popular that a large backlog of orders developed. It was decided that all orders would be cut off on December 31, but all back orders would be produced. Production on the complex piece continued until May of 1981.

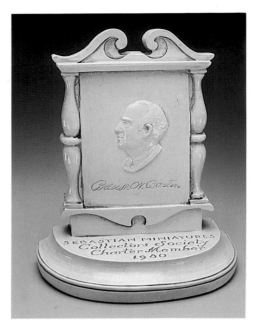

SML 381 Society Membership Plaque 1980 381 LR 1980
  (*Charter Year—1980*)
SML 381-A (*1981*)   381-A LR 1981
SML 381-B (*1982*)   381-B LR 1982

The Sebastian Miniatures Collectors Society was formed in January, 1980. As part of a new member's package, every charter member who joined before December 31, 1980, received a Charter Member plaque with Baston's profile and the words "Sebastian Miniature Collectors Society: Charter Member —1980." Every plaque was hand-signed on the back by Prescott Baston.

Subsequent plaques for new members were inscribed with the year of first subscription.

SML 382 Margaret and Sam Houston 1980 LR 1980–Present
             (No. 2000)

Beginning in 1958 (see SML 285), Baston had combined several of his old pairs on an ornate common base and sold them through the retail line. In July, 1980, Baston combined his 1939 Margaret and Sam Houston (SML 15 and 16) to join this popular series.

SML 383 Coronado and Senora 1980 LR 1980–Present
             (No. 2001)

In July, 1980, Baston combined his 1939 Coronado and Coronado's Senora (SML 13 and 14) onto his "Famous Couples" base (see SML 285). The miniature is sold through the retail line.

SML 384 Buffalo Bill and Annie Oakley 1980 LR 1980–Present
             (No. 2002)

In 1939, Baston designed Buffalo Bill and Annie Oakley (SML 31 and 32) as a set of famous couples for sale to retail stores through Carbone. In 1958, he combined several of his early pairs on a common base (see SML 285). In July, 1980, he added this Wild West pair to the later couples series.

SML 385 Sailing Days (*Boy*)   1981 LR January 1981 10,000
SML 386 Sailing Days (*Girl*)   (*Limited Edition of 10,000 sets.*
Issued : January 1981.
Fully subscribed the same month)

The fourth limited "Children at Play" set (see SML 369), Sailing Days was planned for introduction at the 1981 Atlantic City China and Glass show. The issue had been announced in the November, 1980, Society newsletter, and the previous three years' issues (Sidewalk Days, Building Days and Snow Days) had only recently been sold-out in August, October and November respectively.

The show had been open one day when the internal sales group in Hudson called to say: "Close all sales. The computer says we've sold over 15,000 sets." The following three months consisted of continuous cutbacks on previous orders and the assignment of allotments to the various national dealers. The three-year history of collector demand for these four sets clearly illustrated what had happened to Sebastian Miniatures as a national collectible.

SML 388 Bringing Home the Tree   1981 C 1981 10,000

An Old Marblehead studio account book entry lists: "Feb. 8, 1951; L. A. Bigelow; Sales $66.74; Accts. Rec.: $66.74."After severing relationships with Carbone and Schmid, this was the first entry of personal sales to a gift shop still actively selling Sebastians. The store owner was Paul Blair, then owner of the Salem gift shop and now in charge, with his son Leo, of the Blair's Hallmark stores in the Boston area.

In September, 1980, the Blairs commissioned a series of five annual Christmas scenes depicting a turn-of-the-century Christmas as an annual limited edition of 10,000.

SML 387 Family Reads Aloud   1981 LR 1981
(*Discontinued forever on December 31, 1981*)

The third in the annual "America Remembers" series (see SML 371), Baston portrayed the Victorian family gathered around the family wood stove on a winter night. The father is reading aloud to the family while the mother is sewing. The model for the stove is located in Woody Baston's Wayland home.

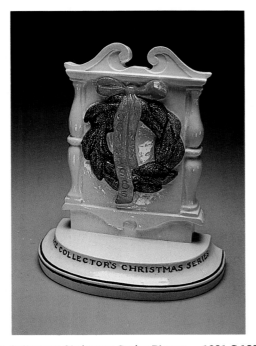

SML 389 Collectors Christmas Series Plaque   1981 C 1981–1985

The Collectors Christmas Series Plaque was commissioned by Blair's (see SML 382) and is designed to accompany the five-year Victorian Christmas series. The plaque will be discontinued forever on December 31, 1985.

SML 390 First Kite   1981 LR Sept. 1981–Sept. 1982
                                     (*Discontinued forever on Sept. 30, 1982*)

First Kite is the first Sebastian Miniature not designed by Prescott W. Baston. After several years of tentative innuendo, Prescott W. Baston, Jr. (Woody) was persuaded to sculpt his own first Sebastian design. Baston assisted Woody in the mold-making and first cast in the old Marblehead studio, but the sculpting, design and color is pure PWB Junior.

The first of a planned series of a father teaching his son a number of "firsts," the miniature was introduced at a Wayside Country Store (Marlboro, Massachusetts) open house in September, 1981, and discontinued forever on September 30, 1982.

SML 392 Forty-Niner   1981 LR 1981–Present
                                     (No. 2347)

In 1849, while establishing a sawmill for John Sutter near Coloma, California, James W. Marshall discovered gold and touched off the California gold rush. The forty-niners, as the gold rush miners were called, came in droves, spurred by the promise of fabulous riches. With the gold rush came a large increase in population and a pressing need for civil government. A year later, California became a state.

In this first of a series, "The Men Who Made America," Prescott Baston, Jr. portrayed this forty-niner, one foot in a mountain stream, panning for the precious metal. The miniature is sold through retail stores.

SML 391 Self-Portrait   1981 LR 1981–Present
                                     (No. 2312)

Norman Rockwell, the famed Massachusetts painter of American nostalgia, painted a humorous self-portrait of himself painting himself while he studies his image in a mirror. In 1981, Baston created his sculpted version of the same theme. In this design, the Marblehead sculptor sits back in his old chair with his legs propped up on the trusty footstool, examining a miniature of himself sitting back in his old chair . . . etc., etc. This wonderful design was introduced in 1982 and will be distributed continuously through all his retail stores.

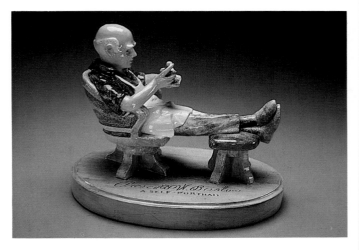

SML 393 School Days (*Boy*)   1982 LR Jan. 1982 10,000
SML 394 School Days (*Girl*)   (*Limited Edition of 10,000 sets.*
                                     Issued: January 1982.
                                     Fully Subscribed at issue)

The fifth limited "Children at Play" set (see SML 369), School Days was allocated as a limited edition of 10,000 sets and fully subscribed before formal introduction to the collecting public.

Baston's design portrays a mischievous young boy preparing to hurl a spitball from behind an old-fashioned school desk top at his sister who is dutifully reciting her lesson.

SML 395 Family Fishing   **1982 LR 1982**
(Discontinued forever on December 31, 1982)

The fourth in the annual "America Remembers" series (see SML 371), Baston portrayed the mother in the process of reeling-in a fish while sitting on the bank of a stream. The son is attempting to net the catch while the daughter is excitedly spurring him on. The father gently supports the mother. The miniature scene is completed with a fish box, tackle box, extra fish poles and tangled lines.

SEBASTIAN PLATES

(8½″ diameter)

Prescott Baston had designed large and miniature figurines, plaques and even Christmas ornaments. He had never produced a Sebastian Miniatures plate. In February, 1978, a snowstorm destroyed Motif No. 1, the Rockport, Massachusetts fishing shack reputed to be "the most-painted scene in America." Baston had sold his own Motif No. 1 miniature since 1950 (SML 161). The Rockport Artists League asked him to contribute his talents to raise funds for restoring the famous building.

He created a bas relief portrait of the Rockport scene, cast it in bonded porcelain, and Lance rimmed it with cast fine pewter. Issued as a limited edition of 10,000, the sales resulted in a substantial contribution to the League. The building was soon restored.

The first of three "America's Favorite Scenes" series, Motif was followed by 1979's "Grand Canyon" and 1980's "Lone Cypress" (Monterey, California), the last sculpted by Hudson sculptor Philip DeNino. The series is now closed.

SP 1 Motif No. 1
   Subject: The old fishing shack in Rockport, Massachusetts, reputed to be the most-painted scene in America.
   Issue Year: 1978
   Issue Limit: 10,000
   Status: Active (No. 6501)

SP 2 Grand Canyon
   Subject: A colorful section of Arizona's Grand Canyon where the Colorado River has cut a deep trench.
   Issue Year: 1979
   Issue Limit: 10,000
   Status: Active (No. 6504)

SP 3 Lone Cypress
   Subject: The lone cypress tree on the Pacific coastline in Monterey, California.
   Issue Year: 1980
   Issue Limit: 10,000
   Status: Active (No. 6511)

(6″ diameter)

Many Sebastian Miniature collectors also collect limited edition plates. Following the success of the Motif No. 1 plate, Baston was repeatedly asked to put his most popular figurines into plate form. In 1980 he responded with his most popular miniature, 1947's "In the Candy Store" (SML 90). Issued in a limited edition of 15,000, the plate center is painted bonded porcelain and the rim is cast and buffed fine pewter.

Planning an annual series ("There was a Time"), Baston followed with 1954's "Doctor" (SML 245) in 1981 and 1953's "Little Mother" (SML 213) in 1982. This series is active, with annual releases of limited editions of 15,000.

SP 4 In the Candy Store
   Issue Year: 1980
   Issue Limit: 15,000
   Status: Active (No. 6505)

SP 5 Doctor
   Issue Year: 1981
   Issue Limit: 15,000
   Status: Active (No. 2103)

SP 6 Little Mother
   Issue Year: 1982
   Issue Limit: 15,000
   Status: Active (No. 2224)

LARGE CERAMASTONE FIGURES

Prescott Baston sculpted many designs in Ceramastone that are not true Sebastian Miniatures. All of these designs are six inches high or taller, or their scale is so exaggerated that they simply do not look like Sebastian Miniatures. Many were distributed widely, some were made to be converted into porcelain, some were speculative models and some were cast in Ceramastone that later appeared in pewter. All of these designs have two things in common: first, all designs were made in Ceramastone and second, at least one is known to be in the private collection of at least one collector. These designs are illustrated and described for collector identification purposes.

LC 1 Paul Revere Plaque   1939

A bronzed plaque showing Baston's Paul Revere statue in bas relief. It stands 7" high and bears the inscription originally appearing on the Baston sculpture. About 250 made for sale by Carbone as a decorative item.

LC 9 Breton Man   1940
LC 10 Breton Woman

Quimper, the French town in Brittany, is famous for its distinctive pottery (quimper or Brittany ware). Carbone distributed a line of quimper ware in 1940 and asked Baston to produce 100 pairs of a Breton couple for in-store display. The man is 10½" high.

LC 12 Woody at Three   1948

Baston planned to make a sculpture of Woody every year, tracing his growth. Following this first unfinished effort (of which he cast five), he became too busy with retail business and commercial designs. "Besides," he adds, "Woody refused to hold still."

LC 2 Jesus   1940
LC 3 Mary
LC 4 Caroler
LC 5 Candleholder
LC 6 Lamb
LC 7 Basket
LC 8 Horn of Plenty

A contemporary Nativity requested by Carbone and sold through retail stores for several years. A modern Mary and Jesus form the focus with Mary approximately 5½" high. Five contemporary "angels" depict (left to right) a caroler, a small candleholder, a shepherd with lamb, a girl with basket and a girl carrying a horn filled with grapes, a banana, apple and pineapple. Baston sold approximately 500 complete sets and 1,000 Mother and Child sets.

LC 11 Large Victorian Couple   1947

Baston designed the R. H. Stearns miniature couple in 1947 (SML 87) to sell during that store's 100th anniversary. He produced 50 large versions for display throughout the store and then an additional 100 in 1948 for display in his retail stores. In August, 1981, during research for this book, Baston and the author found a set of molds for this piece that were unexplainably in beautiful condition. We decided to re-offer the design in 1982 to today's dealers, once again, and 35 years later, for store display. The design is so in demand that it is now available to dealers and collectors (No. 2447).

LC 13 Jell-O Cow Milk Pitcher   1956

In 1956, at the conclusion of his five-year Sebastian Miniature series for Jell-O (see SML 197), Baston designed a cow with its tail as the handle and mouth as the spout. Jell-O had 100,000 pieces fired in porcelain in Japan and offered as a cereal milk pitcher for $1.00 and a coupon from national Jell-O ads.

LC 14 Swift Instrument Co. Girl   1958

The Swift Instrument Company in Boston produced ship and home barometers. In 1958, Swift designed a small barometer to be sold in gift stores. Baston designed a girl in a typical sailing outfit and Swift mounted the barometer to the figurine. The girl stands 6″ high and Baston produced 200 of them.

LC 15 Wasp Plaque   1959

The U.S.S. Wasp was one of the great aircraft carriers in American World War II naval history. When a group staged a reunion for officers and crewmen from the New England area, they asked Baston to produce a plaque to commemorate the event. He produced 100 designs illustrating a wasp "stinging" a Japanese ship.

LC 16 Henry VIII   1963
LC 17 Anne Boleyn

In 1963, both Sebastian Miniatures and the M. I. Hummel figurines (manufactured by Goebel, West Germany) were distributed by Schmid in the United States. In a prophetically unique combination, Baston and Goebel proposed a collaboration of Baston's popular themes and Goebel's fired ceramic production capability. After a few sets of four groupings were fired from Baston's Ceramastone designs, both parties decided against further collaboration.

In this first grouping, Henry VIII and Anne Boleyn are large in Ceramastone and smaller in porcelain. The base of Henry VIII shows the historic joining of Prescott Baston and the Hummel "bee." The figures are 9–10 inches high.

LC 18 Tom Sawyer   1963
LC 19 Mending Time

In another Baston-Goebel collaboration (see LC 16), Baston portrayed Tom Sawyer and Aunt Polly (characterized in the base as "Mending Time").

LC 20 David Copperfield   1963
LC 21 Dora

Another Baston-Goebel collaboration (see LC 16), Baston portrays his favorite David Copperfield from Charles Dickens' family.

LC 22 George Washington Toby Jug   1963
LC 23 Abraham Lincoln Toby Jug
LC 24 John F. Kennedy Toby Jug

Baston designed three presidential heads for ceramic firing into Toby jugs. Lincoln was completed, but November's assassination of President Kennedy ended all progress on the project.

LC 25 Colonial Boy   1964
LC 26 Colonial Man
LC 27 Colonial Woman
LC 28 Colonial Girl

In this final Baston-Goebel collaboration (see LC 16), Baston sculpted a Colonial family costumed in traditional Williamsburg garb.

LC 29 IBM Mother　　　　　　　**1964**
LC 30 IBM Father
LC 31 IBM Son
LC 32 IBM Woman
LC 33 IBM Photographer

The New York World's Fair was held in Flushing Meadows in 1964. IBM commissioned Baston to sculpt and paint 17 sets of two families for use in IBM regional offices displaying models of the World's Fair IBM exhibit. In this starkly realistic grouping of two families, Baston exhibits his uncanny ability for detailed miniaturization. The men are about six inches high.

LC 34 New England Home for　　**1965**
**　　　　Little Wanderers**

Boston's New England Home for Little Wanderers wanted a suitable award for persons working with the child society. Baston sculpted a brother and sister, with doll and panda bear, given shelter by the home. He produced 300 which were mounted on a wooden base and then personalized in a brass plaque on the base.

LC 35 Stanley Music Box　　　　**1965**

Stanley Home Products ordered the design of a baby and base.

Baston's finished design was sent to Japan and 25,000 bisque porcelain figurines were mounted on music box mechanisms. Stanley advertised it as an "Enchanting new premium. A beautiful, delightful addition to your home. Coupon Point Value 750, $2.50 net."

LC 36 The Dentist　　　　　　　**1965**

Baston also designed a dentist working on a young boy, hoping that Stanley would accept it along with the baby and piano. Nothing came of the proposal and only a few prototypes are in existence.

LC 37 Guitarist　　　　　　　　**1966**

Baston designed a large (9″) figure of a boy perched on a stool playing his guitar. Schmid had several thousand porcelains fired in Japan and distributed them through their retail shops.

LC 38 Infant of Prague　　　　　**1967**

A stranger came to the Marblehead studio and discussed the appeal of an American-made "Infant of Prague," a highly-popular icon in Roman Catholicism. Baston agreed to a design of "about $300 worth." The man paid him in cash and left.

Baston sculpted an original and cast six prototypes. A few months later, a detective came to Marblehead and said he had traced the stranger's activities. The money Baston had been paid had been stolen in a spectacular Plymouth (Mass.) postal robbery. Baston asked if he could keep the money. "Certainly," the detective replied, "You've earned it."

LC 43 Minuteman 1975

Baston sculpted a prototype of a minuteman loading his musket for Royal Worcester. The 6½" high figure was never sold as a pewter sculpture.

LC 39 Potter 1973–1975
LC 40 Cabinet Maker
LC 41 Blacksmith
LC 42 Clockmaker

Baston designed four figures for Royal Worcester to be cast into pewter (see p. 147). He cast several prototypes of each in Ceramastone.

LC 44 Mt. Rushmore 1978

Baston sculpted a large (5" high) Mt. Rushmore grouping for the Mountain Company in South Dakota. The grouping was considered too large and he scaled the replica down to a Sebastian Miniature (see SML 372) which has since sold through retail stores.

PEWTER FIGURINES

In 1969, the then-infant Lance Corporation in Hudson, Massachusetts was seeking sculptors to create small figurines to be cast into fine pewter. Ray Kennedy, Lance president, asked Baston if he would agree to allow some of his miniatures to be cast into pewter. The long and unforeseen collaboration had begun.

Baston's pewter work was divided into two areas: general Hudson figurines and the Royal Worcester set of four Colonial Craftsmen. Hudson was Lance's own tradename and the company also cast Royal Worcester's issues.

Baston's pewter was very popular during the Bicentennial marketing period but has declined since then in favor of cuter, more generalized gift themes. It is only since 1981 that Baston pewters have become collector's items.

PF 1 Lexington Minuteman *(Wood Base)*
PF 2 Concord Minuteman *(Wood Base)*
PF 3 Christopher Columbus *(Wood Base)*

In 1969, Lance cast Baston's Lexington Minuteman (SML 361), Concord Minuteman (SML 360), and Christopher Columbus (SML 176) into fine pewter. Then they attached the three figurines to small wooden bases and sold them as gifts through retail stores. Two small pewter plaques were attached to the Minutemen bases. The Concord plaque reads: "Here once the embattled farmers stood and fired the shot heard round the world," and the Lexington plaque reads: "Stand your ground! Don't fire unless fired upon. But if they want a war, let it begin here."

The figurines were soon (1971) taken off their wooden bases and sold simply as pewter. Relatively few mounted on wood were sold.

PF 4 Lexington Minuteman *(SML 361)*
PF 5 Concord Minuteman *(SML 360)*
PF 6 George Washington/Cannon *(SML 84)*
PF 7 Lincoln Memorial *(SML 291)*
PF 8 John Hancock *(New Design)*
PF 9 Colonial Blacksmith *(SML 262-A)*
PF 10 Betsy Ross *(SML 129)*
PF 11 Memotomy Indian *(SML 119)*

From 1970 to 1972, Baston modified seven of his Sebastian Miniatures so the details could be seen in pewter instead of bright colors. He added a new John Hancock for the coming Bicentennial celebration. Lance sold thousands and thousands of these figures until July, 1976, when interest declined. Four of these Hudson pewters have been discontinued and four are still in active production:

	Hudson Model No.
Lexington Minuteman	902
Concord Minuteman	907
Lincoln Memorial	900
Menotomy Indian	905

Figurines	Bells
PF 12 Franklin *(SML 198)*	**PF 17**
PF 13 Jefferson *(SML 124)*	**PF 18**
PF 14 Washington *(SML 84)*	**PF 19**
PF 15 Adams *(New)*	**PF 20**
PF 16 Madison *(New)*	**PF 21**

In 1972, Baston modified three Sebastians and created a new Adams and Madison into a series of "Fathers of the American Revolution." Thousands of sets of these figurines were sold during the Bicentennial period. In 1974, the five bases were modified to fit on the top of five porcelain bell bodies as a Bicentennial bell set. Relatively few (less than 500 sets) were sold. All ten models were discontinued in 1977.

PF 22 Declaration Wall Plaque

In 1975, Lance designed a pine wall plaque with pedestals for Franklin (PF 12), Jefferson (PF 13) and Washington (PF 14) surrounding a pewter plaque bearing the cast replica of the original Declaration of Independence (see PP 7). The plaque was introduced too late in the Bicentennial sales period and only 100 were sold.

PF 23 Washington's Letter of Acceptance
PF 24 Lincoln's Gettysburg Address
PF 25 Lee's Ninth General Order

As the Bicentennial drew to an end, Lance planned a series of America's important documents. In cooperation with the U.S. Library of Congress, the company obtained accurate copies of Lincoln's Gettysburg address, Washington's acceptance of the U.S. Presidency and Robert E. Lee's message to his troops after Appomattox ordering them to return home. All documents were in the men's handwriting.

Pewter plaques were cast for each document and affixed to a wood base adjacent to Baston's figurines. He created Lee by removing the horse from his Sebastian Miniature (SML 359). The plaques were relatively expensive and only a few hundred of each plaque were sold. The series was discontinued in 1977.

PF 26 The Favored Scholar *(SML 193)*
PF 27 Neighboring Pews *(SML 194)*
PF 28 Weighing the Baby *(SML 195)*

Baston sculpted three Rogers Groups (see SML 193) in 1952. In 1975, Lance cast these three designs in fine pewter and Baston added further detail to the crisp metal. The result was an extraordinarily beautiful group of miniature sculptures.

The difference in casting molten metal and liquid Ceramastone requires that the pewter scene be broken down into castable parts. Each element "shrinks" in the casting process, and it was found impossible to rejoin them with solder without destroying the effect of the fragile scenes. Unfortunately, only six sets were produced before the project was shelved.

PF 29 Spirit of '76

Baston's Marblehead studio is only a few hundred yards away from Abbot Hall, home of Archibald Willard's "Spirit of '76" painting. In 1948, Baston designed the first of his Spirit of '76 Sebastian Miniatures (SML 112).

When the New England Council of Governors requested that Lance produce a pewter Spirit of '76 for presentation to President Gerald Ford and the six New England governors in 1975, Baston responded with the famous trio. Only a dozen were produced.

PF 30 Potter *(1973)*
PF 31 Cabinetmaker *(1973)*
PF 32 Blacksmith *(1973)*
PF 33 Clockmaker *(1975)*

Royal Worcester is a British-based producer of fine china and porcelain. The Royal Worcester United States marketing division asked Baston and Lance to produce a series of three pewter sculptures for offer as Bicentennial limited edition commemoratives. Baston designed a potter, cabinetmaker and blacksmith and the series was placed in fine stores around the country. 500 sets were sold and, in 1975, Baston added a Clockmaker to the group. The sculptures are large (approximately eight inches high) and heavy, but Baston's design work is memorable for its composition, detail and graceful form.

PEWTER PLATES

America's Bicentennial celebration was approaching, and Royal Worcester, the British porcelain and china producer, wanted an all-American collector plate series worthy of the event. They contracted Baston to sculpt the series and Lance to cast it in fine pewter. The five-year series (1972-1976) was a highly-popular issue and is positioned today in the Bradford Hall of Fame.

Baston designed another series for Royal Worcester, the Currier & Ives four-plate series (1974-1977) and the beginning of another historical series by Hudson Pewter (1973-1978), with the now-famous "American Independence" plate (1973-1976).

"Bradex No." in the following listing is the permanent number assigned by the Bradford Exchange, the Chicago based international plate broker. "PC No." is the permanent number assigned by the *Plate Collector* magazine listing service.

PP 1 Boston Tea Party (1972)
Issue: 10,000 Subscribed: 10,000
Bradex No.: 84-R76-1.1
PC No.: R78.1.72

The first in the Worcester Pewter "Birth of a Nation" series, the plate depicts the Boston Tea Party which occurred in Boston harbor on December 16, 1773.

PP 3 Incident at Concord Bridge (1974)
Issue: 10,000 Subscribed: 10,000
Bradex No.: 84-R76-1.3
PC No.: R78.1.74

The third in the Worcester Pewter "Birth of a Nation" series, the plate depicts the battle at Concord Bridge, April 19, 1775.

PP 5 Washington Crossing the Delaware (1976)
Issue: 10,000 Subscribed: 10,000
Bradex No.: 84-R76-1.5
PC No.: R78.1.76

The fifth and final plate in Worcester Pewter's "Birth of a Nation" series, the plate portrays in pewter bas relief the famous painting of Washington crossing the Delaware River on December 25, 1776.

PP 2 The Ride of Paul Revere (1973)
Issue: 10,000 Subscribed: 10,000
Bradex No.: 84-R76-1.2
PC No.: R78.1.73

The second in the "Birth of a Nation" series, the plate depicts the ride of Paul Revere, Boston, April 18, 1775.

PP 4 Signing of the Declaration of Independence (1975)
Issue: 10,000 Subscribed: 10,000
Bradex No.: 84-R76-1.4
PC No.: R78.1.75

The fourth plate in the "Birth of a Nation" series, this plate depicts seven drafters and signers of the American Declaration of Independence in Philadelphia on July 4, 1776.

PP 6 Washington's Inauguration (1977)
Issue: 7,500 Subscribed: 1,250

Following the highly popular and successful "Birth of a Nation" Bicentennial series, Royal Worcester planned an "American Historical Series" as an annual continuation. The first plate, issued in 1977, portrays the inauguration on April 30, 1789 of our first president. The series ended with this plate.

PP 7 American Independence (1973–1976)
Issue: Unlimited   Subscribed: 18,462
PC No.: H 30.1.73

In 1973, Baston designed a Bicentennial commemorative plate that was cast into Hudson pewter. The center depicted a bas relief sculpture of the Spirit of '76 and five scenes on the rim depict (left to right) Paul Revere's ride, the Lexington Minuteman, the signing of the Declaration of Independence, the encampment at Valley Forge and Washington crossing the Delaware. The plate reverse bears an incredibly detailed microminiature casting of the Declaration of Independence including all signatories.

The plate was issued as an unlimited edition and, during its four-year life, was subscribed at 18,500 plates before it was discontinued forever on July 5, 1976.

PP 9 American Expansion (1977)
Issue: 10,000   Subscribed: 2,250

Following the highly successful "American Independence" plate (PP 7), Hudson planned an annual continuation of limited edition plates. The 1977 issue, "American Expansion," depicted six events occurring between the Revolutionary and Civil Wars. The center has a group of Forty-niners panning for gold in California and the rim depicts (left to right) a Yankee Clipper, Conestoga wagon, the signing of the Louisiana Purchase, Lewis and Clark and the Alamo. The back bears the names of the 34 states admitted to the Union before the Civil War. Kansas in 1861 is the last.

The plate was discontinued forever on December 31, 1978.

PP 11 The Road, Winter (1974)
Issue: 10,000   Subscribed: 5,750
Bradford: Over-the-Counter
PC No.: R78.2.74

Royal Worcester, the British porcelain and china producer, planned a series of four limited edition Currier & Ives plates beginning in 1974. Working from an 1853 Nathaniel Currier print, Baston sculpted the bas relief "Road" and Lance cast it into Worcester Pewter. The plate was discontinued forever in July, 1977.

PP 8 Spirit of '76 (6" Plate)
Issue: Unlimited   Subscribed: 4,812

In 1975, Hudson used the center bas relief of Baston's "American Independence" plate (PP 7) and cast it into a six-inch pewter rim. Almost 5,000 were purchased before the plate was discontinued forever on July 4, 1977.

PP 10 American War Between the States
(1978)
Issue: 10,000   Subscribed: 825

The second continuation of the Hudson pewter American History series, this plate depicts Lee's surrender to Grant at Appomattox Court House in 1865. The rim portrays (left to right) the firing on Ft. Sumter, boys going off to war, the battle at Gettysburg, the Monitor and Merrimac and President Lincoln delivering his address at Gettysburg. The back of the plate bears the words of the Address.

The plate was discontinued forever on December 31, 1978.

PP 12 Old Grist Mill (1975)
Issue: 10,000   Subscribed: 3,200
Bradford: Over-the-Counter
PC No.: R78.2.75

Baston designed his second Currier & Ives plate from an 1864 Currier & Ives print. The plate was discontinued forever in July, 1977.

PP 13 Winter Pastime (1976)
Issue: 10,000   Subscribed: 1,500
Bradford: Over-the-Counter
PC No.: R78.2.76

The third in the Worcester Currier & Ives series was Baston's "Winter Pastime" from an 1855 Nathaniel Currier print. The plate was discontinued forever in July, 1977.

PP 14 Home to Thanksgiving (1977)
Issue: 10,000   Subscribed: 546

The last Worcester Currier & Ives plate was taken from an 1867 Currier & Ives print titled "Home to Thanksgiving." The plate was discontinued forever in July, 1977.

Chronology and Timeline

Prescott Woodbury Baston was born March 28, 1909 at 9 Court Street, Arlington, Massachusetts. That same year, William Howard Taft was sworn in as President. The 16th Amendment to the Constitution placing a federal tax on all income was sent to the 46 states for ratification and the profile of Abraham Lincoln replaced an Indian head on the United States penny.

Henry Steele Commager, the American historian, states that: "Facts take on meaning only in connection with a hundred or a thousand other facts. By themselves, facts are like bricks, lying around in hopeless disarray. It is only when the historian fits them together in some formal design that they build a harmonious structure. It is here that comparative chronology has its special function to perform. Chronology provides the latitude and longitude of History. It is to History what the multiplication tables are to mathematics, what grammar is to literature, and what scales are to music. It imposes order on that which is otherwise anarchical."

In our attempt to impose order on that span of 45 years since Baston designed his first Sebastian Miniatures to the present, we will parallel significant facts of Sebastian history with historical events that help us relate Sebastian history to our personal lives.

SEBASTIAN MINIATURES		AMERICAN AND WORLD EVENTS
Baston designs Shaker couple as private commission for Woburn restaurant. Begins designs of eight Early Pairs for Carbone. Converts Arlington basement to Sebastian Studio.	**1938**	Adolf Hitler annexes Austria. Orson Welles scares country with radio broadcast of Martian invasion. Newcomer Bob Hope gains national prominence in the movie "Big Broadcast of 1938."
Sebastian Miniatures introduced at Boston Gift Show in March by Carbone. Designs second set of eight Early Pairs. Carbone salesmen begin selling Sebastians nationally.	**1939**	Hitler invades Poland beginning World War II. World Fairs in New York City and San Francisco. Rookie Joe DiMaggio joins the New York Yankees.
Second set of eight Early Pairs introduced at Boston Gift Show in March. Baston's gift business grows as German and Italian imports are curtailed. Designs seven large figures for contemporary Nativity scene.	**1940**	Blitzkrieg in Europe as Norway, Denmark, Belgium and France fall to Germany. Battle of Britain, with heavy bombing of British Isles. Franklin Delano Roosevelt defeats Wendell Wilkie for unprecedented third term.
Designs birds and kittens for Carbone. Begins using "home painters" in Sebastian production. Marries Marjorie Keyes on December 21.	**1941**	Lend Lease to Great Britain. Atlantic Charter declared. Japanese bomb Pearl Harbor December 7; United States enters World War II.
The Bastons move from Arlington to an apartment in Cambridge. Baston volunteers for war job in MIT laboratory. Designs German Band for Carbone.	**1942**	General Jimmy Doolittle bombs Tokyo. Lt. General Dwight Eisenhower commands U.S. troops in North Africa. U.S. home front placed on strict rationing (gas, cigarettes, meat, butter, etc.).
Baston continues work at MIT. Marjorie continues supervision in Arlington studio. Bastons move to another apartment in Winchester.	**1943**	Germans driven from North Africa. Sicily invaded by Allies. Mussolini resigns as dictator.
Baston takes job with J. W. Greer Company, producing miniature components under a wartime subcontract to Raytheon.	**1944**	D-Day in France. Barnum & Bailey Circus fire in Hartford, Connecticut. Roosevelt defeats Thomas E. Dewey for fourth term.
Prescott W. Baston, Jr. ("Woody") born on January 24. Baston resigns war job at Greer and goes back to fulltime work at studio.	**1945**	FDR dies; Truman becomes President. Hitler commits suicide; V-E Day. United States drops atom bomb on Hiroshima and Nagasaki; V-J Day.
Bastons move to Marblehead. Designs Dickens Family for Carbone. Signs contract for "Little Folks" with Schmid Bros.	**1946**	UN opens. Second Nuremberg War Trial. Churchill coins the phrase "Iron Curtain."

SEBASTIAN MINIATURES		AMERICAN AND WORLD EVENTS
Designs Washington, Lincoln and Roosevelt as part of his Famous Americans series. Designs R. H. Stearns series. Begins design of Shakespearean series.	**1947**	United States invokes Truman Doctrine. Palestine partitioned by British. Jackie Robinson becomes first black major league baseball player.
Designs Mark Twain series. Begins Jordan Marsh Observer commissions. Produces Democratic/G.O.P. Victory pair.	**1948**	Indian Leader Mohandas Gandhi assassinated. Alger Hiss–Whittaker Chambers trial. Truman upset victor over Dewey.
Baston designs Santa Claus figurine for R. H. Macy. Designs Paul Bunyan and Clown. Designs three nursery rhyme miniatures.	**1949**	Berlin Blockade lifted. Joe Louis resigns after 12 years as heavyweight champion. Milton Berle becomes first television star.
Concludes design of Washington Irving series of six. Designs Mr. Obocell, to last 15 years and 45,000 pieces. Ends distribution contracts with Carbone and Schmid Bros.	**1950**	Korean War begins. Brink's robbery in Boston. Two Puerto Ricans attempt Truman assassination.
Appoints H. P. and H. F. Hunt as local sales group. Chiquita Banana begins New York City ad agency commercial business. Designs and produces WEEI series.	**1951**	Truman fires General MacArthur. Estes Kefauver conducts crime hearings on T.V. Bobby Thompson hits last inning homer to win NL pennant for New York Giants.
Begins Jell-O series (13 designs over next five years). Charles Dickens figurine completes Dickens Collection (since 1946). Rogers Group series of three designed.	**1952**	King George dies; Princess Elizabeth becomes Queen. Korean War ends. Eisenhower and Nixon elected President and Vice President.
Cancels Hunt Brothers contract and hires Thomas Wiles for local gift shop sales and Copley Advertising Company for direct mail sales. Designs Godey Children series.	**1953**	Mt. Everest climbed by Hillary and Tenzing. Coronation of Queen Elizabeth. Kinsey Report published.
Intensive design, production, sales and personal appearance activities. Designs "Nativity" for Plummers in New York City. Designs first "Doctor" as commercial commission for Irwin Neisler.	**1954**	Army/McCarthy hearing. Fall of Dienbienphu and Indo-China Armistice. Roger Bannister runs sub-four-minute mile.
Designs Davy Crockett to capitalize on national coonskin hat craze. Designs Jell-O Giraffe, Woman in the Shoe and Santa.	**1955**	Khrushchev establishes power in Russia. President Eisenhower suffers heart attack. Unknown bandleader Lawrence Welk airs first television show.
Completes Jell-O series with Three Little Kittens. Designs and produces seven miniatures for Johnson & Johnson. Designs Mrs. Obocell to complement 1950's Mr. Obocell.	**1956**	Russians squash Hungarian Revolt. Elvis Presley becomes national sensation. Eisenhower defeats Stevenson second time.
Designs Jamestown series of four. Designs Nabisco Spoonmen and Buffalo Bee. Designs Mayflower.	**1957**	Russians put Sputnik in orbit. Little Rock, Arkansas dispute and national Civil Rights Movement. Newly-franchised Milwaukee Braves beat New York Yankees in World Series.
Mounts seven early couples on common bases. Begins converting old gift shop figurines into ball-point penholders (until 1967). Designs popular Lincoln Memorial and Shoemaker figurines.	**1958**	Charles De Gaulle elected president of France. Fidel Castro takes power in Cuba. Pope Pius XII dies; Roncali elected Pope John XXIII.

SEBASTIAN MINIATURES		AMERICAN AND WORLD EVENTS
Begins series of *Reader's Digest* commissions. Designs figurines for Museum of City of New York. Designs popular Colonial Bell Ringer.	**1959**	Jet travel begins with Boeing 707 scheduling. Alaska and Hawaii become 49th and 50th states. Charles Van Doren exposed for TV quiz show dishonesty.
Completes Museum of New York series. Designs Son of the Desert for Shriners. Pritchard sells Sebastians in Chicago.	**1960**	Lunch counter sit-ins begin in South. U2 pilot Gary Powers shot down. John F. Kennedy defeats Richard Nixon for presidency.
Separates Nativity into Manger, Wisemen and Shepherds. Designs Savin' Sandy for McNeill Labs. Designs Pope John XXIII and St. Jude for Pritchard Chicago contracts.	**1961**	Construction of Berlin Wall. Alan Shepard first American in space. Roger Maris hits 61 home runs.
Sets Sebastian design speed record with Big Brother Bob Emery. Designs Blue Belle Highlander (later The Piper).	**1962**	John Glenn orbits earth. Cuban missile crisis. Seattle World's Fair.
Second sales contract with Schmid Bros. Ten prototypes with Goebel. Kennedy Toby Jugs cancelled because of assassination.	**1963**	President Kennedy assassinated in Dallas by Lee Harvey Oswald. Pope John XXIII dies; Pope Paul VI installed. Johnny Carson hosts Tonight Show for first time.
Designs family groups for IBM's World Fair exhibits.	**1964**	Khrushchev out; Brezhnev in. Lyndon B. Johnson defeats Barry Goldwater. Beatles appear on Ed Sullivan show.
Designs Pope Paul VI as commercial aftermath of Pope's U.S. visit.	**1965**	Vietnam War deepens. Pope Paul VI visits U.S. First fixed satellite television broadcast.
Designs Dickens Collection base. Designs Little George for Nashville bank.	**1966**	Stokeley Carmichael and Black Power. Medicare becomes law.
Designs Doc Berry. Ends sales contract with Schmid Bros. Designs Uncle Sam.	**1967**	"Flower Children" inhabit Haight-Ashbury district of San Francisco. Israel's Six Day War. Green Bay Packers win Super Bowl I.
Begins design relationship with Lance. Designs Capt. John Parker (Lexington Minuteman) for Bicentennial.	**1968**	Robert Kennedy and Martin Luther King assassinated. Disruptions at Chicago Democratic Convention. Richard Nixon defeats Hubert Humphrey.
Designs Concord and Lexington Minutemen and Christopher Columbus for Lance's Hudson pewter.	**1969**	Neil Armstrong walks on moon. Dwight Eisenhower dies. Woodstock Festival.
Six old Sebastian designs converted into Hudson pewter. Designs Uncle Sam in Orbit for spacewalk.	**1970**	National Guard shooting at Kent State. Vietnam War extends into Cambodia. Charles Manson and the Tate-LaBianca murders.
Designs Diedrich Knickerbocker plaque. Woody Baston hired as Lance pewter production manager.	**1971**	Red China admitted into UN. Pentagon Papers published. Archie Bunker first appears on television.
Designs "Fathers of Revolution" in Hudson pewter. Designs first Royal Worcester Bicentennial plate. Designs George and Martha as Bicentennial pair.	**1972**	Nixon travels to China. Gov. George Wallace shot in Maryland. Nixon defeats McGovern.

SEBASTIAN MINIATURES		AMERICAN AND WORLD EVENTS
Designs three "Colonial Craftsmen" in pewter for Royal Worcester. Designs "American Independence" pewter plate for Hudson.	**1973**	Vietnam War ends. Vice President Spiro Agnew resigns office; Gerald Ford appointed. Watergate investigation heats up.
Designs third Bicentennial plate (Concord Bridge) for Royal Worcester. Begins negotiations with Lance on Sebastian production and distribution.	**1974**	President Nixon resigns; President Gerald Ford and Vice President Nelson Rockefeller. Patricia Hearst kidnapped. Hank Aaron beats Babe Ruth's 714 home run record.
Designs pewter "Spirit of '76" for President Ford. Designs final "Colonial Craftsman" for Royal Worcester. Signs contract with Lance.	**1975**	"Squeaky" Fromme attempts to shoot President Ford. Jimmy Hoffa disappears. "Jaws" top box office movie.
Trains production workers in Hudson. Lance appoints three Sebastian sales groups in New England, New York and Pennsylvania.	**1976**	American Bicentennial. Israeli raid on Entebbe. Jimmy Carter defeats Gerald Ford.
Continued training and expansion of Lance regional sales. "Sebastian Story and Chronology" published. Lexington Minuteman permanently discontinued.	**1977**	Bert Lance resigns Carter cabinet after investigation. Elvis Presley dies. "Roots" on television.
Sebastians introduced nationally at South Bend Collectors Show. Sidewalk Days issued as limited edition. Paul Bunyan discontinued.	**1978**	Pope Paul VI dies; Pope John Paul I and II. California passes Prop 13. Suicide at Jonestown.
Building Days issued as limited edition. Clown discontinued. Baston conducts extensive national appearance tour.	**1979**	Iran seizes U.S. hostages. Three Mile Island accident. Camp David Accords between U.S., Israel and Egypt.
First Edition *Collectors Guide* published. Collectors Society formed. September auction attracts national collector interest.	**1980**	Mount St. Helens erupts. Who shot J.R.? Ronald Reagan defeats Jimmy Carter.
Sailing Days limited edition sold-out before introduction. First national Sebastian Festival in Boxborough, Mass. Woody introduces first Sebastian Miniature, First Kite.	**1981**	Hostages released. President Reagan shot by John Hinckley. Prince Charles marries Lady Diana.
Self-portrait introduced. Family Fishing fourth annual limited Family Series figurine. Limited edition, hardcover *Collectors Guide* published June 12 at second Sebastian Festival.	**1982**	Argentina invades Falkland Islands. Israelis withdraw from Sinai. "Brideshead Revisited" on public television.

INDEX OF SEBASTIAN MINIATURES

(by SML)

Acknowledgements

No book covering this variety of subject matter and breadth of time can be put together without the help of many. After working all these years on what was to result in this volume, I consider it a necessary and pleasant exercise to list the names of key people who, whether they knew it or not, provided much to this history.

My brief attempts at paralleling Sebastian and United States history were made easier by the scholarship of William Manchester *(The Glory and the Dream)* and Elston Brooks *(I've Heard That Song Before)*.

Fellow Lance employees and associates, salesmen, Sebastian dealers and major collectors all played important roles. If they read their names below, they can be certain they are a part of Sebastian history.

Emma Abt	Sherman and Doris Edwards	Kathy Raye
Beverly Albright	Bill English	Hugh Robinson
Roger Anderson	Glenn Gates	Ron Sachetti
Dave Armstrong	Cindy Gavin	Joan and Tony Scerra
Marjorie Keyes Baston	Carol Goonan	Duane Searles
Woody Baston	Joe Havens	Jim Secky
Karl Bjork	Charlotte Judd	Roy Shoults
Paul and Leo Blair	Ray Kennedy	Paul Stark
Russ Bower	Arthur Lowden	Judy Stein
Russ Brett	Terry Masters	Tom Stork
Bob and Elsie Burrows	Charlie Mazza	Martha Vaillancourt
John Caforio	Maureen and Joe Morgan	Jim Waite
Frank Casey	Charles Osenton	Judy Wilson
Doug Cofiell	Don Parker	
Phil DeNino	Mike Parrish	

Unfortunately, I cannot possibly list the nameless thousands of Sebastian collectors who attended the seminars and personal appearances, wrote and telephoned us with questions and answers and, finally, provided an invisible support when my pen was moving most slowly. To all, thank you.

And finally, my thanks to Prescott W. Baston. Without his unfailing willingness to share everything most honestly, this book would not have been possible. Without his incredible creativity and labor for over forty years, this book would not have been necessary.

Glenn S. Johnson
March, 1982

Prescott W. Baston
Marblehead